FOOTPLATE AND SIGNALS

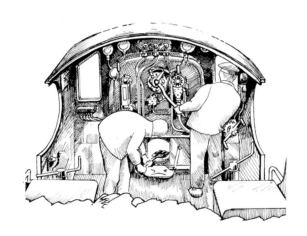

FOOTPLATE AND SIGNALS

The evolution of the locomotive footplate and its relationship with railway signalling and safety

L. F. E. Coombs

· RAILWAY HERITAGE ·
from
The NOSTALGIA Collection

Dedicated to all who had to struggle, bend,
stretch and twist at the controls and tried to understand
confusing signals

First published in 2009

British Library Cataloguing in Publication Data

A catalogue record for this book is available from the British
Library.

ISBN 978 1 85794 319 1

Silver Link Publishing Ltd
The Trundle
Ringstead Road
Great Addington
Kettering
Northants NN14 4BW

Tel/Fax: 01536 330588
email: sales@nostalgiacollection.com
Website: www.nostalgiacollection.com

Printed and bound in the Czech Republic

Frontispiece **Sighting of signals: sometimes a
gantry would carry a mixture of signal types that
included 'somersault' types, the ubiquitous lower-
quadrant and upper-quadrant, and multi-aspect
colour signals.** *Author*

ACKNOWLEDGEMENTS

Grateful thanks are due to R. H. N. Hardy for
commenting on the words, writing the
Foreword and making useful suggestions, as well as
providing some essential photographs; to L. A.
Summers for making a special effort to
photograph important in-cab details and for
advice on some of the illustrations; to David
Holmes, Frank Hornby, Tony Miles, Brian
Morrison and Colin Nash for making their
photographic collections available; to Fredrick
Rich for access to his photo collection and for
valuable comments on the world of the footplate;
to Michael Blakemore, editor of *Backtrack*, for
providing photographs; to Richard Lemon for
advice on signalling matters; to Adrian Clement

of the Institution of Mechanical Engineers and
the Institution of Locomotive Engineers; to the
Signalling Record Society; to Andy Hart of the
SNCF Society; to an anonymous ex-Western
Region signalman for much valuable information;
to my family and, in particular, to Andrew and
Catherine for sorting out problems with the
electronic processing of illustrations; and to Will
Adams, the book's editor, for much advice and
patience, and without whose determination and
attention to detail the book would not have been
published.

   To none of the above is attributed responsibility
for errors or omissions; they remain the
responsibility of the author.

CONTENTS

Foreword 7

Introduction 9

1 The evolution and development of the
    steam locomotive footplate 13
2 'Stop her, back her and keep clear' 23
3 British footplates of the 19th century 47
4 British footplates of the early 20th century 65
5 The locomotive cab in the last 40 years of steam 77
6 British signals and information in the 20th century 101
7 Footplate and signals in words and images 114
8 Other motive power control positions 123

Selected bibliography 126
Index 127

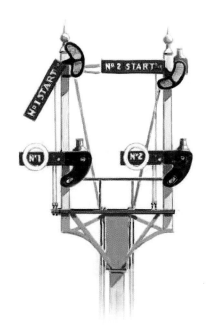

FOREWORD
BY
R. H. N. HARDY

FORMER DISTRICT MOTIVE POWER
SUPERINTENDENT, LIVERPOOL STREET

This is a remarkable book. In the first place, it is written by an ergonomist and I dare say that it is the first of the line. Secondly, the author studies the working conditions of the men who operated locomotives and signals going right back to the earliest days and from a new and critical angle. He will therefore open the eyes of many a reader with a vivid imagination and a thirst for knowledge, and I can assure you that, as a railwayman of 42 years' service and 26 years of retirement by no means idle on railway matters, on nearly every page I have learned some new fact or point of view or noticed something that does not seem to make sense – then, on second thoughts, realised that there might be something in it after all.

Just imagine the operation of a passenger train on the Liverpool & Manchester Railway on a bitterly cold and pitch-dark early evening in 1835. How do you bring your train to a stand at, shall we say, Rainhill? You cannot see the famous landmark, the Skew Bridge, in the dark. On the engine or what passes for a tender you have no brakes, nor is it easy to reverse your engine in the dark to stop in the absence of brakes. You do not have a lifetime of experience and there is every chance that you can neither read nor write, nor do you know much about your steed. Certainly you will have signals of a sort in the shape of

Left **The driver's view ahead when leaning out of the cab of a 'Britannia' 'Pacific'.** *R. H. N. Hardy*

'Policemen', but do they know what lies ahead by day, never mind in the dark? But when you have read the first chapter and used your imagination, you will be wiser and you will understand a little of the appalling conditions under which the early railwaymen were expected to work where human comfort was never remotely considered.

As you move on you will find yourself on the footplate with the enginemen on maybe a Gooch 8-foot Single, a giant in its day, still unbraked but easier to stop by reversing and capable of 70mph with no protection whatever from wind, rain or snow for driver and fireman. As the enginemen inevitably must keep a sharp lookout, they stand, looking ahead along the boiler; if they crouch against the hot firebox for protection, they cannot work or see the way ahead. Who can? Why, the guard perched high up and in charge of other equally frozen brakemen further down the train, who somehow manage to stop the juddering, lurching train and with luck at the station. A hard, hard life, but in tune with the times when men were made of iron.

So read on or maybe dip here and there, for the book lends itself to this, and you come to later days and the author's assessment as a professional ergonomist of the railwaymen's latter-day working conditions. Certainly the signalman carried a grave responsibility, especially with semaphore signalling controlling a highly intensive suburban service. Nor could you always work 'to the book' if such a timetable was to be maintained.

The enginemen usually worked in basic conditions – hard work, coal dust, heat and cold, often no protective cab-doors and, on many engines, some hard riding, rib bruising, rocking and rolling, but safe enough for all that. Now and again you met a driver who refused to take an engine, but the majority were so used to the conditions that, provided the engine did its work, they could put up with a battering. As for me, I gloried in it when I was younger but, in later years as a Shedmaster and District Officer, I did my best to improve matters in so many ways. Nor must one forget those happy days when men had their own engines, shared with another crew or even two other sets of men. Then pride in their engine would remove all obstacles and make the hardest day a pleasure – two enginemen in perfect accord in that private world of the footplate.

There was nothing like the rough and tumble of railway work and the immense satisfaction of a job well done against the odds. Uppermost in your mind was that you were there to run the railway to time, and the fact that this could have been done more comfortably had greater thought been given to the positioning and operation of the various controls never really signified.

Did I ever come across the perfect footplate? Or the perfect signal box? The signalmen at Liverpool Street West Side must have been physically exhausted at the end of the morning or evening peak with a steam-hauled train leaving every 2½ minutes and arrivals and light engine movements galore. To me the perfect signal box was King's Cross Power Box in the 1960s, an oasis of calm yet very much in the centre of things with a supervisor and three signalmen and the linesmen down below working in perfect unison.

And the perfect footplate? Yes, and J. G. Robinson of Gorton had the answer in his tender engines built after 1912. Every fitting, every steam valve, the regulator handle and the reversing gear were perfectly placed. They rode smoothly and had comfortable seats with a clear view ahead. Yet these paragons of virtue were not without blemish, for the shovelling plate was low and the firebox door was high; the firedoor was small, big lumps of coal had to be cracked and the shovel had to be handled and swung in a certain and not easily acquired style so that the coal did not strike the low brick arch and fall in a heap in the middle of the grate. 'Keep your back hand up,' they used to say!

To the ergonomist, signal sighting must have great fascination. But how much do you know about signal sighting or of the association of ideas that leads even the most experienced of men to pass a signal at danger? Every day, the steam-hauled 'Golden Arrow' would pass two semaphore Distant signals at the mouth of tunnels so badly sighted that, as he burst out into daylight, the driver had only a split second to act to make the full brake application that should just enable him to stop at the next signal. Yet no Stewarts Lane driver was reported in my time there for passing the Polhill or Weald Home, and I never had a single complaint about these signals.

Now I must stop, for every page of the book has made me think and remember and learn, and while you may not always agree with the author, it will be a challenge and you will have to think it through, and that will do you no harm at all. As to the association of ideas, it is a fascinating subject and, having nearly come to grief myself back in 1943 through the simplest but most inevitable of mistakes, I know how easily one can get into the very deep trouble from which, maybe, there can be no escape.

INTRODUCTION

One particular feature of Britain's railways in the days of the steam locomotive was what might be called the 'platform enders'. They ranged from the young to the old and their greatest concentration was usually close to the cab of a locomotive about to depart with its train. The cab exerted a certain attraction: many hoped they might be invited to step up inside; others also aspired to be an engine driver and some, less knowledgeable, wondered what all the pipes, levers and wheels were for. The cab of the 'monster' exuded heat and the smell of hot oil and coal dust. Then the driver released the brakes, pulled on the regulator and one of the most atmospheric of all machines came alive – a visual and aural experience that watchers of ships departing and aircraft taking off were deprived of because it was always difficult to get close to bridge or cockpit.

It may come as a surprise to some that it was many years before adequate consideration was given to the control position of the steam locomotive with respect to the needs of the driver and fireman. Time and again the researcher of locomotive design history and operation reads of inadequate and badly positioned controls. In Britain less attention appears to have been given to the subject than in any other country.

Doctors of medicine, and no doubt of law, doctors of divinity, professors of philosophy and many others not directly concerned with the railway, have written at length on railways and their motive power units. There have been many 'railway' authors. The greater number of these have either not been employed by the railway or have had only a tenuous connection. One thing many had in common was their limited attention to the locomotive footplate and the work of the crew. The most respected chroniclers of design and performance tended to relegate the ergonomics and human factors of the footplate to a few paragraphs.

Until the last 50 years, comments in both the technical and lay publications on the equipment and arrangement of the controls and instruments in the locomotive cab are few in number. When gathering facts about their design and their positions, it was very evident that the side on which the driver stood or sat rarely encouraged much comment on the part of writers. For example, within the vast output of O. S. Nock there is not much to be learned about the cab and its equipment, whereas that notable iconoclast Dr Tuplin often included annotated illustrations of locomotive cabs. He had much to say about the levers, valves and wheels of the footplate and how they were placed and used. He wrote in *North Western Steam*:

'The literature of the subject contains very little reference to them [cabs and footplate]. Perhaps this is because in an age of push-buttons it is thought degrading to be acquainted with anything that requires more thought.'

David L. Smith also found space for words on the cab and its controls. R. H. N. Hardy, A. J. Powell and 'Toram Beg' have written at length on the driving, firing and maintenance of steam locomotives. Writing from hands-on experience, they have often referred to details of the footplate. The reader, I suggest, cannot avoid concluding that the footplate crews, about which they wrote, had much to contend with because of badly designed cabs and their controls.

Why did designers and their drawing office staffs often fail to consider adequately the engine crew when arranging the controls? The tendency from the very beginning of railways and for more than 100 years thereafter was to locate individual items in accordance with the mechanical requirements of directness of action and of simplicity. The needs of the human operator of those controls were given secondary consideration. In descriptions of engine driving, one can read of engine crews struggling with awkward and badly located valves, wheels and levers. Not until the advent of the Standard series of locomotives on British Railways was a serious attempt made to study the positioning of the driver's controls so that he could perform his task in comfort and with efficiency.

Irrespective of the way we approach the subject of control on the railway, we cannot avoid considering the human element. For nearly 200 years men and, increasingly in the last century, women have supervised, tended and controlled a system that, until recently, was the principal arterial element and blood of nations. Within the hierarchy and the different skills that could be and were to be found on the railway, the locomotive driver and fireman, together with the signalmen, represented a most important and key element in the conduct of trains.

The majority of 'railway' books have tended to discuss the permanent way and the rolling stock in isolation from the rest of the industrial and social factors of which they were an integral part. Often only a only a few words have been given to the work of railway personnel. The social factors relating to the footplate crew are those of upbringing, education and social standing. The first enginemen were mostly those who were familiar with operating stationary steam engines. Many could neither read nor write. They found themselves in charge of a fire-breathing monster capable of subjected them and their passengers to the hitherto never experienced sensation of travelling faster than a galloping horse. Even in the last decade of the 19th century there were a few enginemen who could neither read nor write, yet they were always masters of their craft. As the different railways of the first half of the 19th century increasingly became more organised, drivers and firemen became part of a semi-military hierarchy in which discipline and loyalty to the company were important aspects of their working lives.

Why does the title of this book include 'Signals'? Because the responsibilities of a steam locomotive driver included the observation of and responses to the information presented by the lineside signals. In some respects he was in a similar situation to that of the pilot of a vessel entering a crowded waterway at night, except with a train he had to respond instantly to an adverse signal and could not steer clear of danger. Just as the steam locomotive took about 50 years to mature, so did a system of lineside signals. The standard system that was finally established in Britain, in about 1890, followed attempts, sometimes unsuccessfully, to operate trains at 50 or more miles per hour using the methods of preventing collisions that had existed in the early years of the steam railway. Faster and heavier trains, and more of them, encouraged the development of better signalling systems, together with automatic continuous brakes, to prevent collisions and to keep the traffic flowing.

In order to explain some of the hazards of railway working it has been necessary to refer in detail to certain accidents and incidents. However, such specific references are included only if they were caused by the failure of a driver to respond correctly to the indications of the signals, or were contributed to by equipment failures in the cab. Unfortunately, the lessons learned from the investigation of accidents were often the only incentive to improve equipment and operating practices. As long as no one was killed and all incidents were of a minor nature, why spend money on equipment that might or might not prevent problems in the future?

The cab of the steam locomotive was a position from which to conduct a train and its passengers safely by observing correctly each signal as it came into view around corners, over the tops of bridges, under bridges, and against a tree, hill or roof background. Fog, smoke and steam often obscured an early view of the signals. In the days of steam the lot of the driver was not an ideal one. Those who romanticised the lives of enginemen did little to further the cause of safety. Reynolds in his *Locomotive Engine Driving* of 1877 provided a more realistic summary of the driver and signal relationship as follows:

'Some signals are badly situated, and cannot be sighted nicely until the engine is close to them. In other instances they can best be seen afar off, across the country; and as the train approaches them they become hid from view by intervening objects. By keeping a good look-out, one man will sight a signal from a point whence another man never thought of looking for it; and in this way, while one is running cautiously for fear that the signal may be turned on at "danger", another having sighted it several miles off is prepared to shut off steam or to run past the signal with full steam on, just as the case may be.'

As the foregoing was written in the late 1870s it is interesting to note that Reynolds uses the expression 'turned on', thus indicating that rotating-board-type signals were still in common use.

For the very good reason that the railways of the world originated in the United Kingdom, this history of the steam locomotive cab perforce concentrates on British practice. However, the cabs, enginemen and signalling systems of France and North America are referred to as examples of two possible directions of development that might have progressed in Britain, albeit that the restricted loading gauge and the unbraked, loose-coupled wagons remained near insurmountable barriers to progress up to the end of steam in this country. High station platforms, together with the 9-foot (sometimes less) width and 13-foot height limits on rolling stock constrained locomotive designers as they tried to develop more powerful engines. In contrast, in France and North America locomotive dimensions were free to expand upward and outward to a much greater degree. With signalling the most significant difference between British practice and the systems of France and North America is the latter countries' use of speed signalling as opposed to the geographical, as will be mentioned further on.

When reference is made to French and American cabs and signals, in order to emphasis

some of the particular lines of development in Britain, the author is well aware that there will be readers whose interests are confined to the British Isles and that anything 'foreign' is either inferior or of no interest. In the history of locomotive development, in particular in the UK, some designers and their design staffs adopted the same isolationist attitude so that foreign ideas were sometimes ignored. In this context 'foreign' can also include the ideas of fellow Chief Mechanical Engineers on other British railways.

The steam locomotive was a machine the operation of which could vary between wide limits. The driver was free to adjust the controls in order to operate the machine most effectively to meet changes in rail surface conditions, such as ice, changes in the gradient and variations in the strength of a side wind on a long train. Operating settings, such as cut-off and regulator opening, had to match train weight and variations in gradient. These factors and others added up to a long list of different combinations of control settings.

Essentially, the driving of a steam locomotive could, on the one hand, be a matter of precision or, on the other, a 'hit and miss' affair. Much of the driving techniques used were based on historical precedent, tradition and evolution from changes in technology, such as the development of the variable cut-off valve gear. However, over 150 years, with only a few exceptions, these changes were gradual. Superheating in the 1900s and the work of Chapelon in the 1930s are examples of step changes that affected the manner in which locomotives were driven and fired.

In endeavouring to describe a standard British steam locomotive and a standard technique for driving it, the relationship between cut-off and regulator, or throttle, opening has to be taken into account. These two principal controls had to be used in combination in such a way to enable a locomotive to be operated most effectively. 'The book' might recommend that the most efficient way to use the power of the boiler was to drive with a wide-open regulator and a short cut-off. However, this ideal theoretical technique was, with some types of locomotives, not the ideal. Too short a cut-off might result in excessive thumping of the big ends and the axleboxes. Therefore with some types of engine a three-quarters-open regulator and a longer cut-off was preferred. The design office might recommend certain control settings, but individual drivers often exercised the freedom to depart from the recommended values. They often based their judgement on the way a locomotive should be driven on how it sounded and felt, as well as consideration for the fireman's back.

The use of the terms 'enginemen' and 'signalmen' is not intended to belittle the fact that the opposite sex has long been part of the railways' workforce and not just a phenomenon of more recent times, albeit that in the UK there have been very few, if any, female drivers of steam locomotives – but there have been many female signalpersons.

In 1804 Richard Trevithick may have been the first driver/fireman of a steam locomotive engine. *Author*

I
THE EVOLUTION AND DEVELOPMENT OF THE STEAM LOCOMOTIVE FOOTPLATE

Before describing the evolution of the locomotive footplate it may be helpful to the reader if first we consider the evolution of the railroad or railway. The railroad was on the scene long before the steam locomotive. A useful opening paragraph for a history starts with 'In the beginning' or 'Once upon a time'. However, neither can be used here because we cannot be certain about how far back in time we have to go to find the ancestor of the railway. A familiar observation in many histories of technology relates to the grooves found in the pavements of Pompeii, the spacing of which matched that of the wheels of a Roman chariot. This dimension was retained for nearly 2,000 years with the result that road vehicles in Britain had their wheels approximately the same distance apart as the Roman chariot. As will be explained, the average dimension of about 4ft 8in came to influence the design of the footplate of the British locomotive steam engine.

TRAMWAYS IN MINES

In the mines of Europe an early form of railway evolved in parallel with road vehicle development. There mankind exercised a natural attempt to ease the physical effort need to push and haul containers of minerals, such as coal. By fitting wheels and laying down parallel runways of timber, the containers could be moved by one man, woman or child more easily and quickly. This became the tramway. No doubt greed eventually entered the equation when the mine-owner insisted that the human 'locomotives' should each move more than one load at a time.

Mining for coal became a major industry in the north-eastern part of England in the last decades of the 18th century. To be profitable the output of the mines had to be conveyed to the sea for onward shipment to where it was needed. This was hampered by a number of rivers that flowed approximately from west to east down to the sea; in doing so they meandered, and over millions of years had cut deep valleys. Therefore the coal from the mines had to be carried up and down steep hills and across the valleys, and this type of topography influenced the need for locomotives, their design and the work of the enginemen.

PLATEWAYS FOR COAL

In 18th-century England wagonways and plateways were used to facilitate the movement of minerals from the mines to the banks of the nearest river for loading minerals, such as coal, into lighters and ships. The wagonways were lengths of timber laid to match the distance between a pair of wheels. Without them the wheels sunk into the mud in winter, while in summer the sun-baked ruts impeded progress. The horse was the power unit. During the second half of the 18th century both plateways and edge rails were in use, particularly in the North East of England. Of the two types of 'road', the edge rail, on which wagons having flanged wheels moved, came to be preferred because, unlike the plateways, the wheels were less liable to be affected by mud and dirt. At the end of the 18th century improvements were made to the edge-type rail.

STEAM POWER

The perfection of the steam engine for operating winding drums and pumps for mine shafts encouraged the further exploitation of coal seams, particularly in the North East of England. Each new mine had to have a means for transporting coal to where it could be loaded on to ships. As mentioned, the profile of the land on the direct routes from mine to river or estuary bank was often severely undulating. Therefore a feature of many of these progenitors of the railroad were steep inclines. Many were self-acting (funicular), operating on the principle that an ascending load was balanced, as far as practicable, by the weight of a descending load. Much ingenuity was exercised in devising systems of ropes and drums for simultaneously hauling up and letting down trains of wagons or chaldrons. The men in charge of the winding engines had to exercise great skill in controlling the trains of wagons as they were hauled up or let down the inclines. Many were potential drivers of stream locomotives. Intervening stretches of line were operated by 'horsepower'. The trains of loaded horse-drawn wagons were 'powered' by gravity on the descending lengths of line. When the wagons reached the start of a descent on some horse-operated lines the horse was unhitched; as the train of wagons moved past, the animal was trained to jump onto a special wagon at the tail end of the train – the 'dandy car'.

PUMPING ENGINES

The application of steam power, such as the pumping engines used to prevent the flooding of mines, required the attendance of an operator. These atmospheric engines (atmospheric because the power was obtained from the condensation of steam) were massive. They usually comprised a number of large timber beams and iron rods together with a boiler and a large-diameter cylinder. In the earliest of these machines the attendant had to open a number of different valves in sequence to effect each individual pumping stroke. Eventually the valves were operated automatically by the machine itself. Thereafter the human element was mainly responsible for keeping the bearings lubricated and the boiler fed with fuel and water. There was no control station

as such. Some of these enginemen would eventually come to drive steam locomotives. Other recruits to the early footplates may have been the intrepid 'convey' men or 'brakemen' that rode the wagons down the inclines and endeavoured, by means of crude brakes, to prevent them 'running away' and being dashed to pieces at the bottom. The development of engines using 'strong' (at pressures greater than atmospheric) steam led to the railway steam locomotive.

THE ONE-TO-ONE RELATIONSHIP

Until the Industrial Revolution there was, except at sea, usually a one-to-one relationship between man and machine or animal. The ploughman controlled the oxen using hand and eye to scribe a straight furrow. The controls were simple and the 'instruments', of what we now call a 'control interface', were his vision of the scene before him. Similarly the driver of a team of coach horses had a simple control interface. However, an important factor in relation to this particular control situation was that of time. Whenever we compare the control practices of one type of vehicle with other types, we have to weigh our comparisons with the rate at which events and changes occur. It is usually a question of whether there is adequate time available in which the operator of a vehicle can react to events and changes and be able to take appropriate control actions. The steam locomotive's ability to proceed much faster than a horse presented its driver and others charged with the safe conduct of passengers and goods with a novel set of circumstances for which there were few precedents. As will be described, the time needed to react to a danger signal, plus the time needed for the brakes to take effect, became important factors with faster and heavier trains from about 1850 onward.

HUMANKIND AND MACHINES

Static machines provided examples of controls either concentrated at one location or dispersed among the mechanisms. Many early factory processing systems were made up of a number of discrete machines, which required the operators or operators to move around; there was no concentration of information and control. Always there had been this balance between the capability of the machine and the abilities of the driver or operator – one or the other had to give way. Either the operator had to stoop and grope to manage the machine. or the design of the machine had to include mechanically complicated rods, levers, bell cranks and springs so that it could be controlled without too great a physical contortion on the part of the operator.

The attitudes of a driver or operator could have a significant effect on the introduction of a machine. We have to recognise that in the closing years of the 18th century in Britain, and for some years after, there were many within the working population who viewed with suspicion any form of machinery; even if it reduced the physical effort of work. Part of any reaction to machines was the fear that they could put men out of work. In the first decade of the 19th century the application of stationary steam engine principles for traction on the railway led to the self-contained, mobile power unit; the locomotive steam engine.

TREVITHICK

The starting point for the development of practicable steam locomotives is usually considered, by those who study industrial history and archaeology, to be Trevithick's steam locomotive of 1804 for hauling wagons on the Penydaren-Abercynon plateway in Wales. However, it does not provide us with an early example of a control position for its driver, nor a footplate – Trevithick had to walk alongside his machine. To feed fuel into the firebox the stoker had to walk backwards and avoid being struck by the mechanism; perhaps this was only undertaken when the machine was stationary.

BLENKINSOP

In the first decade of the 19th century the price of fodder for the hundreds of horses that provided the motive power on rail and road had risen high enough to encourage an alternative. Mine-owners and industrialists turned to machinery, and to steam power in particular. In 1812, the year of Napoleon I's retreat from Moscow, John Blenkinsop devised a steam locomotive intended to circumvent the lack of adhesion sometimes experienced by an iron wheel on an iron rail. His innovative design included vertical cylinders and

connecting rods driving gear wheels. In turn, the gears engaged the single driving wheel on one side of the engine. On the periphery of this wheel were teeth, or rather cogs, that engaged with studs set into the side of the vertical part of the rail.

Illustrations of Blenkinsop's 'rack and pinion' engine do not give a clear indication of where the driver stood to effect control. It may have been that the machine was considered to be a mechanical horse, or 'iron horse', and therefore its driver would walk alongside, as he would with a draught animal. The return-flue boiler had the firedoor at the chimney end, and as we have no certain knowledge about how the engine was operated, we might assume that, like the driver, the fireman would walk alongside. At intervals the engine may have had to be stopped so that the fireman could stoke the fire. Or is it even possible that one person both controlled and stoked? By 1835 the price of fodder fell sufficiently to allow the return of the horse as a provider of motive power, and the Blenkinsop engines and others were put aside to await a rise in the price of fodder, or were abandoned.

HEDLEY

Not until 1825 did a form of footplate enter the history. This was on Hedley's 0-8-0 locomotive, which had a platform at one end for the driver and one at the other end for the fireman; this separation of the crew members was a feature of many of the pre-1830 engines. The word 'footplate' was appropriate at the time because the plate on which the driver stood was often not much larger than his footprint.

Many of the enginemen on the pioneering railways were contracted by the coal mines to move coal by rail at an agreed rate. They also had to supervise the fireman and the workshop mechanic. Both the driver and the fireman had to add grease to the bearings of the coal-carrying chaldrons while on the move. They did this by leaving the locomotive to steam on unattended. They got down, each armed with a long stick on the end of which was a tallow mop. As the wagons passed they applied the grease to the underside of the wagon bearings – a rather hazardous task! When the last wagon had rumbled past, at about 5mph, they climbed on to it. The fireman added fuel to the iron basket of fire hung from the last wagon, which provided an indicator that none of the wagons had come uncoupled. They then started to scramble forward back to the engine from wagon to wagon on top of the coal. Or, considering the low speed of their train, they may have been able to run back to the engine. On rejoining the engine the fireman attended to the fire basket 'headlight' attached to the front of the tender, which was being pushed ahead.

The sight and sound of an approaching train, particularly at night, must have been quite alarming to some bystanders; to others it provided a vision of industrial progress. The basket of fire in front, the open fire door and the sparks shooting up from the tall chimney must have been awe-inspiring, not only to the onlookers but to the crew. The locomotive would hiss and roar. The unsprung wheels of both locomotive and wagons, rolling over the far from smooth rails, produced a cacophony of sound in the otherwise quiet countryside.

'CONTROL INTERFACE'

The early steam locomotives, like their contemporaries the steamships, had what we now term a 'control interface'. In the factories of the late 17th and early 18th centuries the steam engines used to power machinery had evolved from a combination of considered design and convenience of operation. However, there were few, if any, examples of the application of what would now be termed 'ergonomics', a word that came into use in the early 1950s. In the late 18th

and early 19th centuries, controls and control position design was concerned more with the machine than with the human operator. Locomotive designers, such as Trevithick, Hedley, Hackworth and the Stephensons, tried a number of different arrangements of boiler, wheels and cylinders. They had to solve many problems for which there were few precedents, problems that may have been far more important than the type of controls and where they should be placed. Any consideration of the work of controlling a steam locomotive and of the working conditions of the enginemen were most likely secondary matters in the thoughts of those who developed and built the early locomotive steam engines. On the other hand, the early drivers, recruited mostly from the operators of stationary engines, were accustomed to hard work in a harsh world. Therefore they did not expect a life less hazardous and grim than that of the fields, the mines, at sea and the world of factory machines.

STEPHENSON

George Stephenson is often misleadingly credited in 'popular' books as the inventor of the steam locomotive. His contribution to the development of the steam railway was concerned more with adapting the ideas of others into a practicable working method of using steam as a form of motive power. Above all he was ambitious and without fear. A lifetime of 'hands-on' experience enabled him to get to the root of mechanical problems and find workable solutions. His *Locomotion* for the

The replica of the 0-4-0 *Locomotion*: the driver is perched precariously on the narrow platform alongside the boiler and close to the oscillating machinery.
Pendragon

Stockton & Darlington Railway (S&D) had a platform on each side of the boiler on which the driver could stand. It was a precarious workplace. He had to hold on to the few parts of the machinery that did not plunge up and down. The fireman had to stand on the front of a wagon that served as a tender – there was no firing platform as such. Similar driving and firing arrangements were provided by Hackworth on his *Royal George* for the S&D in 1825.

At this point reference can be made to the method of controlling these early engines. The cylinders, piston and connecting rods and the valve gear mechanism were usually close to the hand of the driver. The primary method of control, before opening the throttle valve, was to engage or disengage the gabs of the valve gear and position the valves by hand in order to effect forward or backward movement. And, of course, there was no means for stopping the engine other than shutting off steam and judging the right moment to move the gabs from the 'forward' to the 'reverse' positions.

In 1828 two of the S&D engines suffered boiler explosions, and their drivers were killed. More concern was expressed over the effects of the explosions on property than over the deaths of the drivers – injuries and loss of lives had long been an unfortunate background to human activity. The farms, mines and factories of the Industrial Revolution took their toll and the railways were to add to it. Therefore the deaths of the two drivers has to be viewed against the annual appalling number of deaths of farm labourers, miners, seamen and factory workers. The child mortality rate was high and the expectation of life was very much lower than that of later years.

The boilers of *Locomotion* and *Hope*, two 'Killingworth'-type 0-6-0s, exploded either as the result of material failure or because the drivers had interfered with the safety valves in order to get more power out of their engines. This is where advanced – for its time – machinery come face to face with men having little or no understanding of mechanics and thermodynamics, and most of whom were illiterate. Those that had not been recruited from managing stationary engines obviously understood much about the horses they had walked alongside, as wagons of coal were moved along plateways and railways. But suddenly their fodder-eating horse had been replaced by the

'iron horse', whose workings were both a mystery and a wonder. For some it was a fiery monster. It took either courage or ignorance to stand close to its machinery – possibly a combination of both.

The fear of boiler explosions affected the public perception of the steam railway. Would the 'steam bomb' at the head of their train translate them, in a flash, into oblivion? Even those we would now call 'experts', the advisers to the directors of the proposed Liverpool & Manchester Railway, recommended the use of stationary engines rather than the 'explosive' steam locomotives. These would haul the passenger trains by means of cables. However, once the accountants had done their sums it was realised that the cost of 'fixed' engines and the haulage gear, as opposed to steam locomotives, would be prohibitive. Therefore the scene was set for the famous Rainhill Trials, in which a number of different steam locomotives would compete for the £500 prize, a not inconsiderable sum in terms of the then current price of a loaf of bread.

The conditions under which competing locomotives would be accepted for entry into the Rainhill Trials included the provision of safety valves set to limit boiler pressure to 50psi. There had to be two of these, one of which had to be completely out of the control of the enginemen. Such a condition reflected the general concern at the time over attempts to increase the power of an engine by screwing down or weighting the safety valves. Even later in the century, when drivers had no excuse for not understanding the danger of interfering with the safety valves, some continued to do so. It was not until 1895 that the existing Regulation of Railways Act of 1871 was reinforced by a Statutory Order requiring all locomotive boiler explosions to be reported. Before that time some had gone unreported, other than when they formed part of the evidence considered by a coroner.

A 'MINIMALIST' POLICY

An example of what might be termed a 'minimalist' policy when designing the control position of a locomotive was Bury's 0-4-0 *Liverpool*, as rebuilt in 1831, and intended originally for the Liverpool & Manchester Railway. The footplate was not much bigger than the driver's foot, as it extended back from the

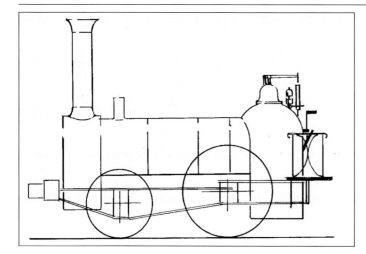

A Bury 2-2-0 of c1830. At the time there was no restriction imposed on the length of an engine, but the designer still provided only a very small footplate. *Author*

firebox by only about 12 inches. A handrail at the side prevented the driver and fireman from falling off. Concern for their safety may not have been uppermost in the minds of the enginemen. Such considerations took second place to their earnings, which on some lines were based on a farthing per ton moved per mile. The farthings soon added up and the men began to earn, for the time, a great deal of money.

Nevertheless, their ability to earn comparatively large sums was constrained by the weak condition of the rails, so they were required to run their trains at a low speed in order to avoid damaging the track. They were also frustrated and lost money because the engines were not very reliable and had to spend time in the workshops. Another requirement was that the driver and fireman had to manage the fire in order to prevent sparks being shot out of the chimney and setting light to crops and trees. The crew of an engine could not evade responsibility for lineside fires because it became customary to number and or name each locomotive.

J. G. H. Warren, in his *A Century of Locomotive Building* (published by Reid in 1923), provides a comprehensive account of the development of the Stephenson locomotives. He includes many of the letters, documents, drawings and illustrations relating to the engines built by Robert Stephenson & Co. Nevertheless, the reader has to search diligently for references to their footplate and controls, or for the methods required to start, control and stop them – there are only a few mentions. At this point it may be appropriate to

suggest that those authors who were engineers, when writing for engineers, may have considered they might insult the intelligence of their readers by describing such matters. One thing is clear from the illustrations selected by Warren – that a footplate for the enginemen was not always included. The accompanying descriptions said nothing or little about where the enginemen had to stand in order to control and to fire.

Few of the books, in addition to Warren's, that have recorded the history of the development of the steam locomotive in the early decades of the 19th century give adequate coverage of the footplate. In 1827 two Prussian engineers toured the works of Robert Stephenson at Darlington and prepared a comprehensive report of their visit. They collected much information about materials, methods of construction and the design of the locomotives examined. However, only a few words were included to describe how the engines would be operated. Nothing was written about the controls and where the enginemen would stand.

Robert Stephenson & Co received orders from the United States for its 'Planet'-type engines. The specification to which they were built apparently did not mention the design of the footplate. Both the British-supplied engines and those made in the USA in the 1830s had short footplates with low railings at the side. The first 'cab' was on a derivation of the Stephenson 'Planet' type for the Camden & Amboy Railroad in 1831. The tender was a four-wheel box-like vehicle with a roof that extended forward over the footplate and therefore might be considered to be the genesis of the American cab.

There are a number of illustrations of locomotives and trains by contemporary early-19th-century artists, both in Warren's book and in others of the early decades of steam railways. The majority of the artists in the non-technical books had only a passing knowledge concerning the shape, elements and working of the engines they portrayed. 'Railway' artists in the 20th century sometimes took the easy path by using clouds of steam to hide those parts they did not understand, while artists at the time of the Stephensons, Blenkinsop and other steam railway pioneers usually omitted what they did not understand. In doing so they deprived industrial archaeologists of important information.

Included in the parts they did not understand was the footplate and its controls. Many of the early pictures, purporting to show a locomotive in action, place the enginemen on the front of the tender. Even had the artists been given access to the official engineering drawings, they would have found, as noted, that very few included details about the footplate. In one example, a watercolour by G. Walker, a Blenkinsop locomotive occupies such a small part of the picture that few details of the mechanism can be made out. However, it does suggest that the enginemen stood on a running board, one on each side of the boiler. What is not included is a tender for carrying fuel and water. This may not be a mistake on the part of the artist because the very early 'iron horses' may have been stopped for 'feed and water'.

One artist in particular recorded his examination of a Stephenson 'Killingworth'-type engine. He wrote:

'I went up to the engine, caught hold of the footboards along which the enginemen walked and stooped to make an examination of its underbelly gearing.'

Photographic illustrations of the Stephenson 0-4-0s used at Killingworth and Hetton show footboards alongside the boiler. They also show four-wheel tenders and side-sheets to the small footplate on the 'Killingworth' engine, but not on the other. However, as these are photographs and therefore taken many years later, they do not accurately record their original state. Running boards, a tender and a footplate would have been added at successive major repairs or rebuilding.

In 1831 *Phoenix* and *North Star* were delivered to the Liverpool & Manchester Railway. These were 'Rocket'-type 0-2-2s, but with the cylinders set close to the horizontal and with a small footplate between them. According to contemporary illustrations, both the driver and the fireman are shown standing on the front of the tender of *Phoenix*. On *North Star* the fireman is on the tender while the driver appears to have one foot on the small footplate and the other on the front of the tender. Around this time Stephenson locomotives were distinguished by a small curved railing at each side of the footplate. Today this would seem to be mere decoration, because it provided little protection for the enginemen to prevent them being thrown off the footplate. A similar decorative feature was sometimes applied in order to rail in the top of the sides of tender.

Francis Anne Kemble was a well-known actress – today she would be one among many thousands who would be called 'celebrities'. In her *Record of Girlhood*, published in 1878, she recalled a visit made in 1831 to the Liverpool & Manchester and being 'introduced' to the engine of the train in which she travelled.

'The reins, bit and bridle of this wonderful beast is a small steel handle, which applies or withdraws the steam from its legs or pistons, so that a child might manage it. The coals, which are its oats, were under the bench, and there was a small glass tube affixed to the boiler, with water in it, which indicates by its fullness or emptiness when the creature wants water, which is immediately conveyed to it from its reservoir.'

Her description of the regulator and its function might seem naïve, but at least she mentions it, whereas so many contemporary writers and those that followed ignored the seemingly mundane subject of how a steam locomotive was controlled.

By this time an important decision was reached for the majority of the new engines, and one that would affect the work of all drivers in the distant future. This was the positioning of the footplate crew, particularly the driver, behind the boiler in the normal direction of running.

In 1831 Robert Stephenson's 'Description

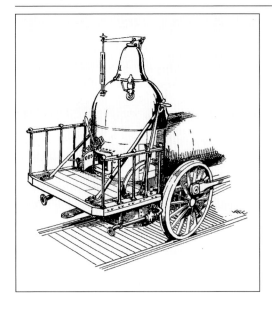

A Norris 4-2-0 of 1840. The footplate is cantilevered from the firebox and similar to that of the Bury 2-2-0. The regulator lever is immediately above the firedoor, and the reverser lever is on the right, the 'coachman's side'. There is one Salter-type safety valve, and the whistle is seated directly on the domed firebox. *Author*

looking platform to which was attached the coupling to the tender. The records do not indicate clearly why the controls were on the left side of the engine and not, as might have been expected at the time, on the right.

THE 'PLANET' 0-2-2

Robert Stephenson's 'Planet'-type 0-2-2, with the cylinders mounted below the smokebox at the front of the engine, and the 0-4-0s evolved from it, provide a convenient point in history to end an era. Most of these engines had a railed-in footplate and the control levers for the valve gear on the right, although some works 'blueprints' indicate that there were exceptions. Frequently, among non-engineering illustrations, 'artist's licence' confuses an attempt to be precise about on which side of the footplate a driver stood.

A 'LIVING' MACHINE

By 1830 the steam locomotive had acquired fully its Stephensonian elements: a boiler with numerous tubes through which passed the hot gases from the fire; a chimney at the opposite end from the firedoor and in which there was a blastpipe to 'draw' the fire; cylinders set close to the horizontal; and a footplate for the enginemen. Essentially the early steam locomotive was a simple vehicle to control. To start with, particularly when compared with other vehicles, it did not have to be steered by its operator. The early locomotives had only three controls: a throttle, a lever for reversing and some method for controlling the supply of water to the boiler. There were no brakes.

One of the earliest technological steps upwards came with the development of valve gears, such as the Stephenson version, which not only enabled a locomotive to be reversed but also provided a means for using the expansive properties of steam most effectively. From the earliest times, the

Book' for *Rocket* included references to a pressure gauge. This was a mercurial gauge fastened to the side of the chimney and extending nearly to its full height. The bottom of the gauge was connected by a copper tube to the boiler. Being concerned that the enginemen might tamper with the safety valves in order to operate the engine at a dangerous pressure value, one of the two valves was enclosed in a casing, which was secured by two padlocks. A water gauge was fixed to one side of the boiler, but details of its type were not included in the description. There were also two water-level test cocks at the side of the boiler close to the chimney end. Even with the comparatively low, by later standards, boiler pressure – about 40-60psi – these test cocks were not always an absolute indicator of water level. If the water level was above that of the cock then it would flash into steam. If the level was below that of the cock then steam would also shoot out. A driver had to distinguish between the two different sounds.

Stephenson's book also describes the method for reversing the engine by lifting the eccentric rod gabs out of gear and moving the rods of the slide valves by hand. The remains of *Rocket*, as exhibited at the Science Museum in London, provided information about both the controls and the footplate. On the left of the small footplate were the levers for reversing the engine. On the back of the boiler and above the firebox was the regulator valve. The footplate was a very flimsy-

Three early footplates. At the top is *Locomotion* of 1825, with a running board but no footplate. The driver had to cling on to those parts of the mechanism that were not moving.

The second drawing depicts *Rocket* of 1829, the progenitor of the traditional footplate. 'Footplate' was an appropriate name, because it was not much bigger than the feet of the driver.

Finally is *Planet* of 1830. The side railings to the footplate appear to have been more decorative than functional. *Author*

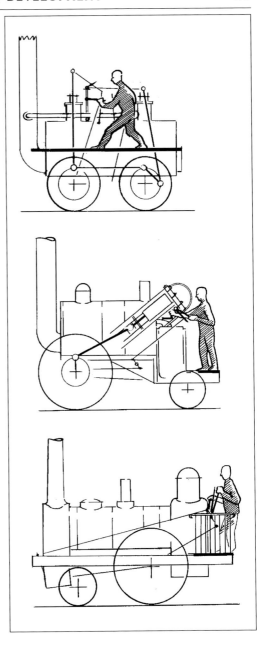

combined variable cut-off and reversing valve gear lever or wheel has usually been referred to as the 'reverser' even though it performs two functions.

STOPPING

Even after the successful development of the steam locomotive, some of the early railways continued to employ horses. Those that were single track had passing loops into which horse-drawn trains could wait to let a steam train pass – steam took precedence over everything. The S&D continued to employ horses for pulling coal trains until 1854.

Additionally, operating rules were laid down. A starting time might be published but not an arrival time because the operation of both horse and steam trains was an uncertain activity. Sometimes on a single line two trains would be in opposition, and one would have to reverse back to the last passing loop. The rule was that the train that reached the halfway marker first prevailed and the other had to reverse. The drivers of both types of trains were made totally responsible for avoiding collisions and for reaching agreement over who should give way to whom. The means for stopping a train were either non-existent or uncertain.

Eventually, greater attention had to be paid to solving the problem of stopping a train. Hitherto the designers and the drivers had concentrated their efforts on getting the engines to start and to keep running for a reasonable distance without breaking down. On the colliery tramways and railways the wagons sometimes had a long pivoted lever that could be pressed down to apply a brake block to one of the wheels. For about the next 30 years brakes were sometimes provided for the tender but rarely on the engine wheels. A well-known photograph of GWR 8-foot Single *Hirondelle* clearly shows that brakes were neither fitted to the engine wheels nor to those of the tender. It was considered a dangerous procedure to apply a brake to the wheels of the engine – the torsional load might break an axle or distort the track. However, the drawings for Stephenson's *Patentee* of 1831 show a steam brake acting upon the wheels of the second and third axles. The brake blocks were referred to at the time as 'clogs' and, to be pedantic, at this point in this history the word should be 'break' rather than 'brake'; not until the 1850s did the latter become the accepted spelling for the action and equipment needed to stop a train.

It was not until 1876 that proper attention was paid to the need for standards relating to the stopping of trains. In that year a report was jointly prepared by the Board of Trade and the railway companies concerning, among other safety matters, brakes. The report noted that the amount of controlling power generally supplied with trains was at the time insufficient, and therefore it was recommended that companies be required by law to provide every train with sufficient brake power to stop absolutely within 500 yards at the highest speed at which it travelled and irrespective of the gradient. The 500-yard value reflected the average top speed and weight of passenger trains; subsequent advances in train weight and speed would overtake the intention of the regulation.

After the Newark Brake Trials of 1875 the Glasgow & South Western Railway (G&SWR) adopted the Westinghouse brake, as did the Caledonian, North British and Great North of Scotland companies. However, in 1885 the G&SWR changed over to the vacuum brake system so as to be in step with the Midland Railway, which, after an argument with the Westinghouse Brake Company, had adopted the rival vacuum brake (the Midland and the G&SWR had the same Chairman). The choice between a pressure brake, such as the Westinghouse, and the vacuum system was not always a technical decision – commercial politics sometimes governed the choice.

The report on an accident to a Manchester, Sheffield & Lincolnshire Railway (MS&L) train in 1884, resulting from a fractured crank axle, criticised the lack of an effective automatic continuous brake. The system in use was the Smith's non-automatic vacuum brake; when the brake hoses ruptured, the brakes were released and not, as with the later systems, automatically applied. The suggestion that the Westinghouse system should have been adopted was met by the comment by the MS&L Chairman, Edward

Watkin, that the Chairman of the Westinghouse company had been a Board of Trade inspector and that was why the Board favoured the Westinghouse brake system.

●

Once fully developed, the steam locomotive required men to work in an environment of movement, vibration, extreme temperature variations and precipitation for which, other than that of the stagecoach driver, there were few precedents. The combination of steam and water under pressure, the noise of the exhaust and of the engine's progress, together with the firedoor in the middle of the 'control' panel, presented the operating crew with a 'living' machine. Victorian writers alluded to 'monsters breathing fire, steam and smoke, their pulsating glare lighting the darkness'. This typical comment on the new arrival on the industrial scene prevailed for many years and to some extent may have engendered the 'elite' attitude of locomotive crews, with the result that they came to accept the arduous working conditions with pride rather than with resentment. Early legislation concerning the operation of locomotives made the driver responsible for opening and closing the gates at level crossings with the highway; failure to do so incurred a 40-shilling fine, which, at the time, was the equivalent to about 480 loaves.

Like Gilbert's policeman, an engineman's lot was not necessarily a happy one. Yet for the first hundred years of the steam railway there was rarely any shortage of recruits for the footplate. The driver and firemen were the elite of the railway fraternity. The driver stood on the open footplate as if he were on the bridge of a steamship. He scanned ahead hoping to sight danger in time to 'whistle for brakes', screw down the tender brakes and, if need be, reverse his engine. Whistling for brakes referred to ordering the brakemen, stationed at intervals along a train, to apply or take off the brakes of the coaches or wagons. Such a method of controlling a train could still be found in use in the 1880s.

2
'STOP HER, BACK HER AND KEEP CLEAR'

'White is right, red is wrong,
Green is gently come along.'

From a Victorian child's book quoted in
Rixon Bucknall's *Railway Memories*, 1947

THE VIEW AHEAD

Before considering the evolution of the cab, from
the earliest footplates to the enclosed cabs in the
last quarter of the 19th century, attention has to
be given to the operating conditions, safety
equipment and signalling that had to be provided
or improved. These in turn affected the design and
equipment of the footplate as well as the
responsibilities of the enginemen.

This review of early railway operation is
concerned not so much with how the various
signalling systems worked but with what the driver
saw, how he interpreted what he saw and how he
acted upon the information. In other words, the
subject is considered from the point of view of the
driver. The term 'view ahead' is intended to
embrace all the information gathered by an engine
crew from watching the state of the line ahead,
and any other visual or aural information.

Many books and articles on railway operation
and on the work of the driver have tended to treat
signalling as one subject and driving as another.
Much has been written about signals and
signalling in general but, it is suggested, little has
been written about the visual task of the driver;
particularly in the days of steam. Therefore this
book is concerned less with the role of the
signalmen and their equipment than with the

information provided or not provided to the driver
by the lineside, fixed, signals. Signal boxes, their
equipment and the mechanisms of the lineside
signals have been covered by authors better
qualified than this writer to discourse on the
subject.

The driver of a steam locomotive was in control
of a machine whose speed could be regulated in
order to comply with the operating timetable on to
which was superimposed the instructions of the
signalling system. The signal-to-driver
information link was one of visual perception by
the driver. Of course, 'perception' is not just what
the eyes see but how the brain interprets the
information. Sometimes they were not in accord.
What the driver saw or did not see was often a
paramount question to be answered at an inquiry
into an incident or accident.

Essentially, the visual task was that of watching
for obstructions on the track and for the
indications of lineside signals, if any of the latter
were provided. Obstructions could, of course,
include other trains. Descriptions of operating
conditions on the early railways in the days before
lineside signals tell of locomotives and their crews
being sent out to look for and help a disabled train.
Sometimes they were sent 'wrong line' and may
have sighted the steam and smoke of the train they
were looking for coming towards them.

The railway was treated by some as if it were the
Queen's Highway – in other words, free to be used
by all. This conception of the freedom of the
highway was vigorously defended, and lingered on
in Britain in the shape of the private-owner, unbraked, loose-coupled coal wagons that became a

'Stop her, back her and keep clear.' In an emergency and without any form of brake on the engine, all that remained was to 'whistle' for brakes to be applied by the guard and the brakesmen and to endeavour to reverse the engine. *Author*

handicap to faster and more efficient ways of moving bulk freight. By the end of a day, even if there was a timetable, frequent breakdowns and derailments resulted in trains taking many hours longer to reach their destinations than was intended. In the days before lineside signals a driver might shut off steam in order to listen for the sound of another train that might be ahead, or even for one that might be getting too close on his tail.

RUSHING INTO A DARK VOID

Safety often depended very much upon a driver's intimate knowledge of the road ahead and his ability to know exactly how far his train had proceeded since passing the last landmark. In daylight this was rarely a problem, but at night in driving rain or snow he had a difficult visual and spatial task. Away from cities and towns there were few lights. On a moonless night a train would be rushing into an apparently dark void. A driver needed the mental ability to deduce his position, reinforced by the distinguishing sounds made when passing under or over bridges. A driver's knowledge of the timetable and the movement of other trains could prove invaluable when, for example, a train on the other line was expected to be passed at a certain location; its non-appearance would prompt a driver to slow his train and be ready to encounter a derailment that may have spread across both lines. As in modern times, a driver could do little to protect his train if the track immediately ahead was suddenly obstructed by an accident to another train, by a tree blown down or a collapsed bridge. The consequences of all such events were governed primarily by the distance the driver could see ahead and by the time it would take to bring his train to a stop.

TIMETABLE WORKING

Up until about 1840 the number of trains moving along a particular route was not usually great and, as already explained, drivers were ever alert to the presence of conflicting trains and could take steps to avoid collisions. In addition, passenger train speeds averaged only about 20mph. However, the reliability of locomotives and rolling stock was not good; delays were frequent and these sometimes made a nonsense of any timetable working.

Those drivers who did not own a pocket watch regulated the progress of their train by observing the station clocks as they passed by. In the 1840s and for some years after, the regulation of station clocks was uncertain. 'Railway Time', that is London (Greenwich) Time, was not always adhered to, and a Station Master might continue to set his clock to local 'sun' time. This situation could result in a station clock, either through custom or through error, being some minutes ahead or behind Railway Time. Mistakes made in setting individual station clocks, together with errors made by drivers when trying to maintain point-to-point timings, could accumulate to an extent that it became inevitable that an engineman could be driving his train on the assumption that the preceding train was a safe distance ahead. By 1850 Greenwich Time became the standard for all railway clocks.

EARLY LINESIDE SIGNALS

On the pioneer railways the 'policemen', stationed at intervals along the line, protected train movements by displaying hand and arm signals. On some of the railways the arm signals were as follows: both arms raised indicated 'stop'; one arm held vertically meant 'all clear'; and one arm pointing horizontally indicated 'slow down'. On other lines 'stop' was indicated by the arm held horizontally and 'proceed' when held vertically.

SAFETY IN STATIONS

When approaching a station at night in the 1830s and '40s, the driver of a train hoped that the line was clear into the station and that the points had been correctly set. Sometimes at night he had to rely upon someone placing a lighted lamp or a candle in a window to indicate that it was safe to proceed. Increased train weight and speed prompted the adoption of lineside signalling. At night the policemen used lanterns that could present a red light for 'stop', a green for 'caution' and white for 'all clear'. The colour shown depended on how much time had elapsed since the last train had passed. This was the 'time-interval' system of avoiding rear-end collisions, and was to some extent satisfactory when the maximum speed was about 30mph. However, a train with a limited ability to stop and on a down gradient was a lethal 'missile' to any other train in its path. Depending on the local circumstances, such as the presence of a tunnel ahead, the person charged with operating the time-interval signal turned it to the 'proceed' position a set time after the last train had passed, the assumption being that the interval for a particular section of track was that required by the majority of trains to reach the protection of the next signal. Of course, there were many reasons why the system was not foolproof. For one, if a train were to come to a stand in the section ahead its only protection, once the section time has elapsed, was for one of its guards going back along the line armed with a flag to warn the following train to stop. This method of train protection remained in use until the last quarter of the 19th century.

The early railway stations were a collection of disparate items: buildings, track, points, and turnplates or turntables. The operation of the points was not always coordinated. The driver of a train approaching a station had to have some indication that the points were set correctly, that there were no wagons or carriages standing at the platform, that there were no road vehicles or people encroaching onto the tracks and that the station as a whole was ready to receive the train. At stations where there were a number of turnouts and crossovers, each worked by a local lever, pointsmen set the different routes under the orders of the Station Master. At one location a pair of points was normally set to lead into the sidings of the yard; if a train needed to be directed into the station a pointsman had to sit on the weighted lever to keep the points reversed – should he relax his position the train could be derailed. Drivers had to be on the lookout for stub-type turnouts, which, if run through in the trailing direction, would derail a train if they had not been set

correctly. One of J. C. Bourne's engravings clearly shows this type of turnout.

This is where the history of the early years of signalling is rather indistinct because each railway and sometimes each of its stations had different ideas about how to indicate to an approaching train that the line was clear. The thing that came readily to hand was a pole or mast to the top of which could be hoisted a flag or object such as a ball (hence the American term 'high ball'). A driver on approaching a station would look out for the 'all right' signal. The principal disadvantage of a flag was its dependence on the wind to keep it flying at a right-angle to the track – no wind, no signal.

So what was a good shape for a signal? The question did not arise where speeds were low; despite the lack of effective and reliable brakes, an alert driver could avoid a collision even if the only warning given might be a policeman's flag. The need for signals designed for the purpose only became acute when speeds and the weight of trains began to increase, even though, at the same time, no improvement was being made in the means for stopping quickly. One criterion for a signal was that it had to stand out against a confusing background of trees, buildings and overbridges – this was one reason why signals were often mounted at the top of tall masts.

Contemporary signal systems of the 1840s and '50s that might have provided models for the shape of signals were the Admiralty horizontal rotating-board arrays on the top of hills that formed a communications chain between London and Portsmouth; the six-arm semaphore stations of the visual telegraph between Anglesey and Liverpool; and the French Chappe telegraph stations, whose semaphore arms would eventually become the precursor for the ubiquitous moving-

Familiar shapes available for use as rotating-board signals compared against a background. In order to provide both an early indication of a signal's message and to be able to distinguish it from its background, many signals were mounted on high masts.
Author

arm railway signals. The Royal Navy also used moving-arm signals on ships.

A driver was required to spot a signal at a distance and therefore much depended on the visibility conditions. Snow and fog and the real world of the footplate could make a nonsense of any attempt to apply a scientific study of the subject. The urban environment in particular provided a combination of vertical, horizontal and inclined shapes or lines. However, it included few circular shapes, other than the wheel. Therefore a round shape or disc stood out against such a background, and this shape was adopted for some railways. Another familiar shape was that of the barred gate, in particular the turnpike. A horizontal bar by its very nature and through decades of use instantly, in most people's mind, meant 'stop'. Another familiar and everyday shape was that of the weather vane, from which may have been derived the 'fishtail' signals. One advantage of these three signals was the simplicity of mounting. All that was needed was a vertical shaft to which the signal was fixed and thus could be turned 'on' or 'off'. By 1845 most companies had adopted the colours for boards and lamps of red, green and white to indicate respectively 'stop', 'caution' and 'line clear'. Why the choice of red and green? Of the two, the human eye is more sensitive to the latter. Whether or not the order of colour preference of the majority – blue, green, red, purple, orange, yellow – influenced the choice of red and green is not known. At the same time we have to remember that in the early decades of the 19th century the range of durable colours was limited.

Red had long been associated with danger. Therefore, right to the end of mechanical signals in railway history red was the 'danger' colour, and was presumably chosen because it was associated with danger in other activities. However, the only other extensive use of red and green was to be found at sea, with the former for port and the latter for starboard; red appearing to starboard required a vessel to 'stop, back or keep clear', but if it appeared to port then it meant 'stand on'. In other words it could either mean danger or safety. Therefore the nautical use of red may not have necessarily influenced the choice of that colour as the danger signal on the railway.

The origin of the choice of green as a 'caution' colour is not clear. In Britain in the 1910s and '20s it began to be replaced by yellow, although it continued in use by shunters, whose steady green light indicated that a driver should slow down, or, as from the early days, 'gently come along'. Until the end of the traditional British manual signal box a signalman would display a green flag or light as an indication to the driver of an approaching train that, irrespective of other signals, he should proceed with caution. It also remained the 'caution' colour in France until the 1930s.

To avoid inadvertently employing drivers and others whose sight may be 'blind' to one or more colours, various tests were applied, although the most important requirement for drivers was the ability to distinguish red, green and, in the 20th century, yellow from other colours. Few railway companies used actual signals as test targets. A frequently used test required a candidate to sort out a specified colour from a pile of different-coloured lengths of wool. Other tests required a candidate to distinguish different shapes and mixtures of colours. The latter led eventually to the now familiar Ishihara cards on which sets of differently coloured dots are arranged in such a way that numbers and shapes are formed from red and green dots. Anyone with defective colour vision cannot distinguish them from the background dots.

The Liverpool & Manchester Railway in 1834 used rotating signals that, in the 'turned on' position, presented a board face-on with decorative ends. At night the lamp mounted above the board, and turning with it, showed red when the board was 'turned on' and white when 'turned off'.

Brunel of the Great Western is credited with introducing the 'disc and crossbar'-type signal. The red crossbar, when turned to face an oncoming train, indicated 'stop'. When it was turned through 90 degrees to the 'off' position the red disc on the same shaft then faced the train to indicate 'proceed'. With the GWR disc and crossbar signal the down-line crossbar was distinguished from that of the up line by its downward projecting ends. Both the crossbar and the disc were perforated in order to prevent the signal being turned by a strong wind. Crossbar-type signals remained in use even after the semaphore-arm signals had become the British standard – at least one was still in use in the early 1960s.

The London & South Western Railway (L&SWR) used a signal that combined the indications for a pair of tracks in one disc – in effect it was a 'four position' signal. When both the up and the down lines were blocked the signal presented a half red disc. If both lines were clear the disc was turned edge-on to approaching trains on both lines. If only one line was clear, that half of the disc applying to that line was open. To enable this type of signal to be readily distinguishable it was usually mounted on a tall mast to give a sky background.

Around this time there were other multi-position signals. The operating Rule Book for the Sheffield, Ashton-under-Lyne & Manchester Railway (SA&M) of 1846 refers to the signals provided. These were three-position rotating discs, displaying red for 'stop', green for 'caution' and, when edge-on to an approaching train, 'line clear'. Red, green and white lights respectively were used at night. In parallel with the evolution of the rotating-board signals was the development of the moving-arm types that replicated the arm positions used by railway policemen.

When the board signals that rotated on a vertical shaft came into use they usually had a lever fixed to the shaft so that they could be operated by a policeman standing on the spot. Such was the comparatively leisurely pace of train operation in the 1840s that the policeman might not be stationed at the signal when a train approached. It could be that he was away from the

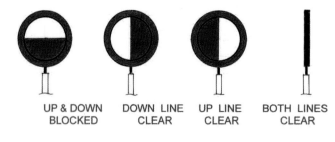

UP & DOWN BLOCKED   DOWN LINE CLEAR   UP LINE CLEAR   BOTH LINES CLEAR

The L&SWR 'four-position' signal combining indications for both down and up lines. *Author*

signal and having difficulty with operating some points. The driver then had recourse to the steam 'trumpet' to announce that he was waiting at the signal. The intelligence of the first policemen/ signalmen was low; many could neither read nor write. Any system of conveying information to the train drivers therefore had to be simple enough to be understood by those who had to operate it as well as those who had to obey the indication. The less intelligent were often preferred because they were less likely to be distracted from their duties by intellectual activities, such as thinking about other matters or even reading.

AUXILIARY OR 'DISTANT' SIGNALS

In the 1840s 'auxiliary' signals came into use to give the driver of a train approaching a station an indication of whether the station signal was 'on' or 'off', or whether there was a train standing at the platform. These were the progenitors of the Distant signal. A common type of auxiliary signal was a disc, and as it was usually positioned a few hundred yards out from a station it was operated remotely by the Station Master or policemen by a lever and wires. On the GWR a rotating fishtail board was used as an auxiliary signal. This was painted green and provided two indications: pointing to the left and facing a train it indicated 'caution', while turned parallel to the line it indicated 'line clear'.

Irrespective of its method of operation and shape, the rules concerning how a driver should respond if the signal was 'on' varied among the different railway companies. Some companies required a driver to stop at an 'on' auxiliary signal and wait for it to clear before entering the station. On others, although the early auxiliary signals repeated the indication of the relevant Home signals, a driver was required to bring his train to a standstill as soon as possible if one was 'on', then proceed ahead with caution, being prepared to stop clear of another train standing at the Home signal or to keep clear of a junction. This

anticipated the permissive block working of later years. Such a method of working continued to be used in France in the 20th century.

With the greater use of lineside signals, be they rotating boards or semaphore arms, came the situation in which a driver not only had to look out for and obey the signals, but also had to know at which point he had to stop his train, which was not necessarily alongside the signal itself. If a station or junction signal, particularly the latter, was 'on', a driver had to stop clear of any turnouts or crossings. The Midland Railway, for example, used a red rotating crossbar board to indicate when all shunting in and out of the sidings to which it referred had to stop. The North Eastern provided a red square rotating-board signal, applying to both directions of running, which, when face-on to approaching trains, indicated that the level crossing gates were open to road traffic.

In 1847 an employee of the North British Railway who was in charge of two signals that were some distance apart decided that he could save much leg work by arranging a system of some wire and a pulley together with a counterweight at one of the signals so that it could be operated remotely. From that time on individual signal levers were increasingly concentrated and interlocked with each other, in one cabin or signal box. From that small beginning would eventually emerge legislation by the Board of Trade requiring that the control and interlocking of signals and points be concentrated wherever practicable. This innovation was of benefit not only to signalmen

Typical night time indications at a station and its auxiliary signals, c1840; white indicates 'proceed', green 'caution', and red 'stop'. There were variations among different railway companies. *Author*

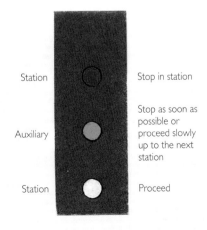

CAUTION

CLEAR

An 'auxiliary' signal on the GWR c1850, showing the 'caution' and 'clear' indications; at night green and white lights respectively were shown. *Author*

but also to drivers, because they could be more certain that there would be no conflicting signals displayed.

Signals were sometimes mounted on tall posts that extended upward from the roof of the signal box. A driver approaching a double-line junction would see four semaphores, two on each post. Unless one of the semaphores on his line was 'off' he had to stop his train clear of the junction. At some double-line junctions, particularly with mixed-gauge tracks, a driver had to 'read' correctly a selection of different types of signal, some rotating-board and some semaphore, as well as flags waved by signalmen.

TO THE LEFT OR TO THE RIGHT?

The relationships that existed between the horseman, the coachman and the side of the road on which vehicles moved when confronted with oncoming traffic in the UK can be related to the development of the typical British semaphore signal, and in particular to its position and movement relative to the track to which it applied.

The 'policemen' whose arm signals indicated to the driver of a train whether or not it was safe to proceed stood at the side of the track, sometimes to the left and at other times to the right. Which was the better from the driver's point of view was not important because on the open footplate the view ahead was as good to the left as it was to the right. The drivers of the majority of early locomotives usually stood on the right, which may have been influenced by the traditional 'coachman's side' – the side that favoured holding the reins in the left hand and the whip in the right. On most British double-track railways the trains moved on the left-hand track in the direction of travel, thereby conforming to the rule of the road on the highway.

With all such rules there are likely to be

exceptions. For example, in 1839 on the Newcastle & Carlisle right-hand running was the rule. Standing on the right also meant that a driver was on the side of an approaching train on the other line and could exchange hand signals with the other driver. At the same time, of course, he was not on the 'platform' side when approaching a station or about to start from one; again, possibly of little importance because a driver was not constrained to a particular side at any one time. A locomotive's controls were not like those of a horse, which required 'hands on' control for most of the time.

In the United Kingdom and France and those countries that also adopted left-hand running, the majority of signals were placed to the left of the track. Although the railway policeman used to hold his arm pointing across the track, the arms of semaphore signals were usually arranged to point away from the track to which they applied. Yet, as already noted, the usual position of the driver on the footplate of British locomotives of the first two decades was to the right (although the driver of *Locomotion* on the S&D in 1825 stood on the left-hand running board, as can be seen with the present-day replica). Eventually the country's railways became divided between those that were right-hand drive and the rest. In 1848 the Caledonian Railway ordered some 2-2-2s from the Vulcan Foundry. These, unlike the majority at the time, had the reversing lever on the left-hand side of the footplate; from then on all new Caledonian locomotives were left-hand drive. Among the big systems that evolved in the 19th century with left-hand drive were the London & North Western, Caledonian, Lancashire & Yorkshire, North British and London, Brighton & South Coast (LB&SCR). In 1854 the Great North of Scotland Railway's first locomotives, from Fairbairn of Manchester, had left-hand drive, as would be all its subsequent engines.

On the continent of Europe the left-hand-running French eventually put the signals on the left. Germany and those countries influenced by its technology adopted right-hand running, with the signals on the right of the track. In North America the engineer's (driver's) position became established on the right and there were few left-hand-drive engines. Sitting on the right, the engineer carried on the coachman tradition of the Old World. However, what was not inherited from the railways of Britain was left-hand running on double-track sections. In North America the rule of the highway is supposed to have originated in the last quarter of the 18th century on the Lancaster Trail through Virginia and Pennsylvania. The teamsters of the Conestoga wagons moving along the trail kept their oxen and wagons to the right when meeting a team coming the other way. Town by town, then state by state, the keep-right rule extended nationwide. Eventually, as the doubling of railroad track became necessary with increasing traffic, right-hand running became the rule. But with all rules there have to be exceptions, such as the Chicago, Lake Shore & Southern, which adopted left-hand running and placed the signals on the left and pointing toward the track.

As a footnote, with the advent of the automobile the sit-on-the-right coachman tradition inherited from the Old World applied. Not until Henry Ford started mass production of cars was the driver's position moved to the left. However, as late as the 1930s expensive 'quality' automobiles in the USA, as in most of Europe, were often right-hand drive.

The position of a signal, to the left or to the right of the track to which it applied, was often dictated by convenience of operation. A typical arrangement at a station would have had the 'up' line and 'down' line signals mounted on a common post or mast. Irrespective of the position of a signal relative to the track to which it referred and to the degree it could be distinguished readily against its background, the driver's detailed knowledge of the route and its signals was an essential part of the overall operating environment. Every driver had to know when and where to expect to catch a first sight of a signal. Only if a driver was unfamiliar with a route would he come upon a signal unexpectedly.

SKY BACKGROUND

The ability to pick out the white light of a 'proceed' signal was not too difficult away from inhabited areas. There were few lights mounted high up, because there were not many tall buildings. However, occasionally a white light or even a red light that had nothing to do with the railway might be mistaken for a signal. David L. Smith, in his *Tales of The Glasgow & South*

On the Great Northern Railway c1900, maximum-height Distant signals provide a sky background – some were more than 60 feet high. The spectacle frames were set lower down. Other than their fishtail ends, the semaphore arms and the lamp spectacles were identical in colour to those of the Home signals to which they referred. *Author*

Western (1961), recounts the occasion when the red light at the end of Girvan pier, far away in the distance, was mistaken for a red signal. A white flag was sometimes used to indicate 'all clear', although there appear to be no examples of white laundry blowing in the wind and misleading a driver. As already noted, to provide in daylight an early view against a sky background some signals were at the top of very tall masts. On the GNR, for example, in the last quarter of the 19th century signals were being mounted as much as 60 feet above rail level. The spectacle plate was usually positioned lower down the mast, and often a duplicate signal arm would be positioned lower down so that it could be seen in fog.

VARIOUS SHAPES

In the 1840s and '50s there were still variations in shape among the signals of the different railway companies. Those responsible for the safe operation of trains by the provision of lineside signals had yet to agree upon what was the best shape and colour for a particular type of signal. Any study of signal shapes and colours that only related to an ideal environment, as exemplified by the designer's drawing board ideas, was more academic than practical. The visual environment, particularly in the urban, industrialised parts of Britain, frequently obscured the lineside signals, to which problem was added that of the smoke of the locomotives themselves. Furthermore, rain, snow and fog could make a driver's signal sighting task that more difficult. A bright, new and clean semaphore blade facing into the sun matched the illustration in the company's signal manual, but it often had to be picked out from a background of the rising or setting sun.

THE ELECTRIC TELEGRAPH

In the late 1830s a driver seeing some form of signal ahead indicating that the line was clear had to place his trust entirely in the Station Master or 'policemen' that it was so. He relied on their strict adherence to the operating rules and, most importantly, to operating the time-interval system. Provided everyone concerned with the operation of trains kept strictly to the rules, the time-interval system of working was not necessarily as dangerous as it might have seemed. Nevertheless, if one person in the chain of command decided to 'cut corners' by ignoring the specified interval, accidents were bound to happen. This is why, when approaching a station or junction, the driver of a train kept it at a slow speed ready to respond to disc signals or semaphores or flags and lights exhibited by the station staff. As mentioned, it was the Station Master's responsibility to ensure that all the turnouts were in the correct position and there were no obstructions in the shape of odd carriages or wagons standing forgotten on the line. In some respects, the arrival of a train was analogous to that of a ship docking, during which process a number of people had to be at their allotted positions and alert for any eventuality.

In 1837, on the Liverpool & Manchester Railway, Fothergill-Cooke demonstrated an electrically operated telegraph system. The company was neither convinced nor impressed. At the time the officials of the railway did not realise that it was the answer to their drivers' concerns over the weakness of using the time-interval method of keeping trains apart. Today there is a tendency to take a superior attitude to such behaviour and ascribe decisions to forego advances in technology as being irresponsible. However, our attitudes, conditions and technical knowledge of today cannot be compared with those of earlier times. Nevertheless, in 1841 the North Derbyshire Railway management, led by Robert Stephenson, took a more enlightened approach and installed a telegraph link through the long Clay Cross Tunnel. This operated in conjunction with a signal that assured drivers that the preceding train was clear of the tunnel. In 1845 the SA&M acquired a Cooke & Wheatstone telegraphic apparatus that enabled the clerks at the stations at each end of the 3-mile-long single-track Woodhead Tunnel to communicate in order to ensure the safe operation of trains. Furthermore a 'token' in the form of a dedicated locomotive, with a powerful headlight, was coupled to the front of all trains before they were allowed to enter the tunnel.

A telegraph system was acquired by the LB&SCR to indicate when the line was clear through Clayton Tunnel. At the time the Brighton main line was controlled on the time-interval system with a minimum permissible interval between trains of five minutes. Here we have an example of three different systems for preventing trains running into each other: time-interval working, the telegraph and lineside signals. The telegraph system through the tunnel and a Distant signal 350 yards out from the signalman's box should have been an effective way of preventing a train entering the south portal of the tunnel before the preceding train had cleared the far end. However, on 25 August 1861 the automatic device that should have returned the Distant signal to the 'on' position failed. The station staff at Brighton, who should have dispatched trains at a minimum interval of five minutes, failed to do so. The signalmen at the two ends of the tunnel exchanged confusing messages. Altogether the circumstances resulted in a rear-end collision in the confines of the tunnel.

Even as late as 1875, in relation to advances in signalling technology, the time-interval method of keeping trains apart was still in use, as evidenced by the report of the inquiry into a collision at Kildwick on the Midland. The report criticised the signalman for allowing an express, which collided with a stationary excursion train, to proceed before five minutes had elapsed since the latter had passed.

FASTER TRAINS

By the 1870s some trains were travelling at 60mph, but the signalling as a whole had not kept pace with the advance in speed. At 60mph a train covers nearly 100 feet each second. If a Distant signal was not observed and responded to and the brakes not applied, the train would be at the Home signal in half a minute. Fog and heavy snow were, in those circumstances, critical elements in the chain of events, each adding to the time factors. Essentially, the weight of trains and their top speeds began to advance faster than the technology of lineside signals. The visual information concerning the state of the line ahead at night presented an entirely different set of

sighting tasks for a driver. Except when close to a signal and in good visibility conditions, a driver depended on being able to pick out the red and white lights from some way off. For the first two decades of the steam railway in Britain the signal lamps shone brightly against a dark background. However, eventually the growth of towns and their buildings, often close to the railway, presented white lights that could be confused with those of the signals.

SPACE-INTERVAL BETTER THAN TIME-INTERVAL

Unfortunately for railway safety in general and the well-being of passengers and enginemen in particular, the telegraph was not rapidly installed by railways as part of a space-interval, as opposed to the time-interval, method of keeping trains apart. Many companies used it just for transmitting company business, at the same time defraying its cost by providing a message service for the public. Eventually, however, the telegraph became the basis of the space-interval 'block' system by means of which only one train was permitted to move through a section of line at a time. It was well understood, but its adoption was often opposed by some railway companies. They argued that their existing methods of operating were safe and adequate. 'A block system would do just that – block the line,' was a typical riposte to the Board of Trade's insistence that the 'absolute block', space-interval, system be installed. As late as 1877, in relation to the advances made in railway technology, a letter in *The Times* for 23 January commented that the Block System appeared to be putting a goods train on the line to form a block, running a fast train into it, then dispatching train after train till all were blocked in, and unable to move backwards or forwards. Such ignorance of railway operation, leading to many letters that took hold of the wrong end of the stick, would not remain just a feature of the Victorian press but would continue to mislead readers to this day.

The august LNWR adopted the electric telegraph in 1854. The 'telegraph' stations were spaced at approximately 2-mile intervals and often coincided with a passenger station. Close to each office were three-position semaphores, one for the down and the other for the up line. The driver of a train approaching one of the semaphores would understand that if the arm hung down vertically then the line as far as the next telegraph station was clear. If the arm was at 45 degrees he knew that the train ahead of him was still in the section and therefore he had to bring his train forward cautiously. If the arm was positioned horizontally, this meant stop, as with other types of signals.

As far as the drivers were concerned this system for preventing tail-end collisions appeared ideal. The 'stop' indication, when strictly applied to prevent a train entering the section ahead until the preceding one had reached the next telegraph station, provided 'absolute block' working – that is, only one train was allowed to be in a section at any one time. However, sometimes those responsible for ensuring that the traffic kept moving decided that 'permissive block' working should be used, otherwise there would be delays to the trains, particularly as there were sometimes big differences in speed between the different classes of train. To operate the line on the 'permissive block' method meant that each signalman could exercise his discretion as to whether to display a 'stop' or 'caution' signal. If an express had just passed, he might display a 'caution' rather than a 'stop' signal if the following train was, for example, a slow freight. Therefore drivers were no longer given an absolute assurance that there was no other train in the section ahead of them. At the same time drivers had the added responsibility when passing a 'caution' signal that they did not let their train go at a speed such that they could not stop clear of any train ahead that may have had to stop in the section, and possibly only a short distance ahead and hidden round a bend.

HEADLAMPS, DISCS AND CODES

With legislation requiring that every mile of railway had to be fenced in, the provision of headlights sufficiently intense to illuminate the track ahead was not considered necessary on the steam railways of Britain. However, lamps came to be carried at night on the front of locomotives to provide a warning of the approach of a train. Later the lamps became part of a code that indicated the type of train. For example, two white lamps on the buffer beam might indicate an express train. On some railways coloured lights were used to give a greater number of possible headcodes. In daylight the unlit lamps served to indicated the classification or intended route of a train approaching a junction. On some railways, large white discs were put in place of the lamps for daytime use.

Holcroft, in his *Great Western Locomotive Practice 1837-1947*, provides a first-hand account of 19th-century signals and headlamp codes.

'The driver invited me to take over on the return trip to Wolverhampton at night, and while he kept a lookout I endeavoured to spot the signals myself. In those days the signal arms on the GWR carried only red glasses whether for stop signals or Distants, and when they dropped to clear a white light was exhibited. In an industrialised area with much street and other lighting it was difficult to pick out the white light at a distance, especially as approaching passenger trains carried a white light for the headcode. More confusion was to be found where the LNWR lines intersected, as their signal lights showed green in the off position where intermediate signal boxes had been cut out on a Sunday, and these could be mistaken for the green or combination of green and white lights in the headcodes carried by GWR goods trains.'

The use of green in headcode lamps was not confusing in the days when that colour indicated 'caution' because it was not used as a 'line clear' indication on the lineside signals. On the MS&L in the 1850s and '60s engines were required to carry a lamp on the offside of the tender that displayed a white light forward and a red light astern. However, at Norton Fitzwarren (GWR) in November 1890 the driver of a special train up from Plymouth was misled by the green headlamp of a goods train engine that was standing in his path and with which his train collided with great force. The signalman had forgotten that he had allowed the goods train to reverse through a trailing crossover and occupy the up line during shunting operations. On the Lancashire & Yorkshire Railway, where there were four main tracks, the rear lamp of a train on the slow line had to display a green light and not a red. This rule required that all tail lamps had to be capable of showing either red or green. Another example of the use of green headlights were those carried on the front of the locomotive heading the funeral train of Queen Victoria in 1901; there were two white lights and two green.

In contrast to British practice, the unfenced right of way in North America made a headlight an essential item. At night, before the introduction of electric lights, the view ahead was reinforced by a large oil lamp that could illuminate the track for about 500 yards. When trains began to operate at 60mph this meant that the engineer could only see ahead a distance equivalent to 15 seconds, which gave little enough time to stop on sighting an obstruction, particularly in the days before the air brake. All the enginemen could do was either crouch down behind the backhead of the firebox and hope that they and the wooden cab were not crushed by the tender in the impending collision, or they could jump for it. However, as top speeds increased in the first quarter of the 20th century, electrically powered headlights became available. Interestingly, as late as 1916 some locomotives on the Pennsylvania Railroad, hauling the fastest trains, did not have electric headlights; presumably as Westinghouse electro-pneumatic automatic block signals protected many of the company's main lines there was less need for them whereas, particularly on single tracks governed only by train orders, electric headlights were most essential.

DISTRACTION AND EXPECTATION

Distraction is a factor in a chain of events that has led to a driver missing a signal. Mechanical problems, such as a burst gauge glass, have diverted the driver's attention so that a signal has come into view and swept by without being spotted. Expectation has proved to be another trap into which a driver could fall. Driving the same train along the same route day after day and never being confronted by an adverse signal could lead the driver to assume that a signal was or would be clear when it was not. Michael Reynolds, in his *Engine Driving Life*, refers to this as 'set'.

SAFETY REGULATIONS

That the early railway was viewed by the public as an unsafe form of transport was contrary to the facts. Only five passengers were killed in accidents

in the 1830s, although there was also an unaccounted-for number of railway servants killed, as well as many maimed. In 1840, however, fifteen passengers lost their lives in accidents. The public's perception and, no doubt, sensational articles in the press influenced Parliament, which led to the Railway Regulation Acts of 1840 and 1842. These established a railway inspectorate within the Board of Trade concerned with improving the safety of operating trains. The primary concerns of drivers at all times was whether they would be able to stop the train quickly in the event of a sudden emergency.

The railway companies, ever mindful of their shareholders, tended to oppose any proposed equipment or systems that could enhance safety but cost money. They based their arguments on the premise that safety equipment, such as more effective brakes and signalling, would engender a false sense of security on the part of enginemen – they would become less alert to potential dangers. Even a member of the Royal Commission of 1874, T. E. Harrison, a notable proponent of safety systems, averred that, as the block system was credited with providing absolute safety, enginemen were led into a false sense of security that might affect their judgement.

Drivers, as with other railwaymen, were liable to find themselves in the dock facing a charge of manslaughter following an accident. Fortunately, for many of them, judges and juries considered that an error of judgement should not necessarily be considered a criminal act. Furthermore, juries were not averse to deciding that, though a driver, for example, had failed to respond correctly to a signal, the railway company, corporately, was guilty of failing to provide a good and unambiguous system of signalling, or in some cases a reliable and effective means for stopping a train quickly. Year by year traffic increased, junctions and stations acquired more complicated pointwork and trains travelled faster. The methods of the 1830s and '40s could not be continued, otherwise the number of accidents and fatalities would increase to an unacceptable level.

DETONATORS

In 1841 E. A. Cooper devised an item of signalling equipment that drew a driver's attention to danger by exploding. This was the detonator, which would remain an essential item of safety equipment on the railways of Britain and other countries for the next 150 years. As with most successful ideas it was simple. An explosive charge and detonating caps were contained in a thin metal case with lead 'tails', which enabled it to be held in position on the top of the rail. The pressure of a wheel would set off the charge. The resulting explosion was intended to be loud enough to be heard by the enginemen on the footplate, however noisy their surroundings. Detonators could be used as an emergency signal to stop a train or, as was most common, for indicating in dense fog to the drivers that the signal they were about to pass was 'on'. The use of detonators was not too expensive, other than the cost in lives of those responsible for crossing the tracks in dense fog and putting them on the line.

The success of the detonator contributed to some extent to holding back the development of expensive and complicated in-cab signalling systems. D. L. Smith, in his *Tales of the Glasgow &*

South Western, recounted the occasion when an inspector found that a driver had no detonators with him. On questioning this failure to abide by the rules, the reply was that he always knew the whereabouts of other trains. This approach to safety was a throw-back to the very early years of the railways when drivers depended very much on knowing where other trains were at a particular time.

BRITISH SIGNALS IN FRANCE

Although this book is concerned primarily with British practices, a few words on the ways in which signals developed in France are apposite, if only because signalling in this country might have continued along the same lines. French lineside signals were derived from the early types used in Britain, and continued in use long after their country of origin had taken a very different approach to the subject. Whereas the majority of the rotating signals used on Britain's railways

The early British disc and board signals influenced French practice. However, France adopted 'speed' signalling and not the later British multi-'doll' 'geographical' arrangement. *Author*

provided a positive 'off' daytime indication, this principle was not applied in France. Except for a white light at night, the discs, squares, diamonds and triangles were edge-on to an approaching train and therefore not easy to pick out from the background. The *mecanicien* (driver), watching the view ahead, proceeded at schedule speed unless confronted by a signal turned face-on. In other words, if there is no signal, proceed. Of course every *mecanicien* had to know the position of every signal.

In France, at night, a red light or lights indicated 'stop', and a white light meant 'proceed'. Until the 1930s green was the 'caution' colour for a Distant or repeater signal. The meaning of a yellow light depended on to which of the independent, pre-1938, companies it belonged.

In 1938 the Est region of the newly constituted SNCF embraced ex-Alsace Lorraine (AL) locomotives. Because the AL had been under German occupation between 1870 and 1918, many of the engines included German features, such as right-hand drive. After 1918 the French did not change the right-hand running rule on double track in Alsace Lorraine and the signals were kept to the right of the line, as in Germany. The result of all this was that a driver in charge of a train going east from Paris came to a point where he had to adjust to being on the right-hand track and to obeying signals over on his right. In practice, no doubt, a change of crew took place at the one-time border. In 1922 the AL received new-built versions of Etat 'Pacifics'. These had right-hand-drive controls in place of the left-hand type of the Etat. In Britain this would have been equivalent to providing the Western Region with right-hand-drive 'Britannias', which of course did not happen.

TWO-POSITION LOWER-QUADRANT SEMAPHORES

The majority of railways in Britain eventually adopted the two-position lower-quadrant semaphore. The three-position semaphore, which had often been part of the time-interval system of train protection (for example, five minutes, ten minutes and 'block clear') fell out of favour, in part because it proved difficult remotely to move the arm precisely to one of the three positions.

Nevertheless, it was still in use in the late 1860s on, for example, the MS&L and the GWR. Forty years later three-position signals returned in the shape of American automatic upper-quadrant semaphores, installed by the LB&SCR, GNR and GCR. These remained in use for only a few years until being superseded by multi-aspect colour light signals.

THE DISTANT SIGNAL

The successor to the auxiliary signal was the Distant signal. The shape and colours of its arm were usually identical with those of a Home signal. From the earliest years of lineside signals, as mentioned, a green light was used as the 'caution' signal and continued for this purpose until the 1890s, when it took the place of a white light for 'off' on both Home and Distant signals. At night the white (later green) and red lamp aspects of a Distant signal were indistinguishable from a Home or absolute stop signal. Provided he was certain of his train's location, a driver could assume that a red light ahead was that of a Distant signal and not that of a Home signal, and therefore he did not need to make an emergency brake application. Depending on circumstances, the early Distant signals were not always interlocked with the relevant Home signals and therefore could be operated independently. Eventually a Distant signal when 'on' indicated that the Home signal ahead, and to which it referred, was also 'on'. On seeing the red light (in later years a yellow light) and the horizontal arm of the Distant signal, a driver knew that he need only make a normal brake application because the line was clear up to the next Home signal and for 440 yards beyond. With a Home and Distant signal co-located, the two vertically disposed red lights at night indicated an absolute stop. The upper light white and the lower red indicated that the signal could be passed but speed had to be reduced because the next signal was 'on'. Two whites meant 'proceed at line speed'. Later, the upper light would be green and the lower red to indicate that the next signal was 'on', and two greens indicated 'proceed at line speed'.

In 1872 the LB&SCR started to use Distant signals that had a distinguishing V-shaped notch at the end of the arm. Later a corresponding white 'V' was painted on the red of the semaphore blade. Subsequently the Board of Trade decreed that

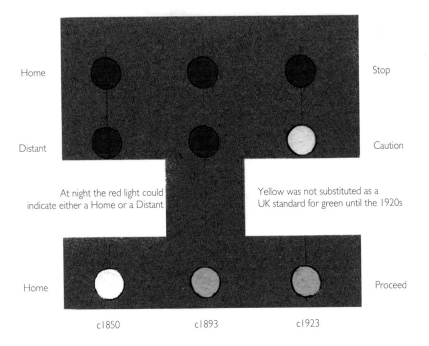

Night indications for a sequence of Distant and Home signals from c1850 onward. Depending on the company, a driver on sighting a green 'caution' signal had to be prepared to bring his train to a standstill as soon as possible even before reaching the next Home signal. *Author*

from 1877 all companies had to cut a 'V' notch into the ends of all semaphore Distant signal arms. At that time the Midland was still using revolving discs, while on the one-time NER a few square rotating-board signals were still to be found in use in the 1960s at level crossings. It would be another 40 or more years, however, before methods were devised to distinguish at night a Distant from a Home signal light. Examples were the Coligny-Welch illuminated 'V' alongside the spectacle plate and, on the Furness Railway, the flashing, gas-lit Distant signals. In 1910 the Metropolitan District started to use yellow as a 'caution' indication, but it was not until 1924 that a yellow light became the national standard for the 'caution' indication at a Distant signal, and for the colour of the arm.

CONFUSION

By the 1870s the railways of Britain as a whole had not only become more numerous but were more complicated. There were more lineside structures, such as overbridges. Signals had to be sighted against a sometimes confusing background of buildings, poles and platform canopies. This combination of shapes presented a visual challenge to a driver. If a signal proved difficult to distinguish it might be given a painted white background. On the GNR massive white wooden 'hoardings' were erected behind some signals. The semaphore arms on some railways were inclined in the 'off' position at about the same angle as that of adjacent roofs. On the LNWR the arms had a languid droop when off – a case of, when 'off', being neither 'on' nor 'off' – whereas on the GWR, GCR and the L&YR, for example, the arms, when pulled 'off', made an angle of 30 degrees to the vertical.

On the GNR, and later in Northern Ireland and Wales, the so-called 'somersault' signal was used. This had an arm whose pivot was halfway along its length. The pivot was also above the centre line of the arm when it was in the horizontal position, so

Typical Home and Distant signals on the LB&SCR. The Brighton company was the first to distinguish a Distant signal arm from that of a Home by the 'V'-shaped end. However, at night its red light could still indicate either a Distant or a Home signal. *Author*

that it was not only balanced, but would also move to the 'on' position should the operating mechanism fail. Edward French devised this type of signal following the triple collision at Abbots Ripton on 21 January 1876. This was caused by the slotted-post-type semaphore signals being frozen in the 'off' position by ice and snow building up in the slots.

OPEN BLOCK AND CLOSED BLOCK

In the first few decades of the block system the signals were kept in the 'off' position until such time as a train passed – this was the 'open block' system of working. Once a train had gone forward past the next block post, the signalman, on receiving 'line clear', would pull his signals 'off', at which position they would remain until another train passed.

The 'closed block' principle of working, which was to become the standard, ensured that semaphores only stood in the 'off' position during the passage of a train and therefore were less likely to become frozen and give a false clear indication as at Abbots Ripton. Despite that, the NER retained slotted-post signals to the end. Relating to the driver's view ahead, the vertical or near vertical blade of the GNR signal when 'off' anticipated that of the three-position signals that were imported from America whose least restrictive indication (vertical) stood out against the background.

With the 'closed block' the signals, after having been put to danger after the passage of a train, remained 'on' until the next train was offered from the signalman to the rear. As far as a driver was concerned, this method of operating the block provided an assurance that each signal had been specifically 'pulled off' for his train and had not been left in the 'off' position after the proceeding train. Nonetheless the 'open block' continued to be used on some railways on the continent of Europe for the next 100 years, notably the Lartigue electro-semaphores in France.

SUBSURFACE SIGNALS

When the Metropolitan Railway opened in 1863 it presented a particular set of safety problems to be solved. The provision of signals was very necessary. At the time, public perception about railway safety tended to be obsessed by the dangers of trains colliding in tunnels. For the greater part of a journey a driver, standing on the open footplate, had to watch out ahead for signals and other trains that might be obscured by the dark of the tunnels, or lingering clouds of steam and smoke. Although the footplates of the Metropolitan and, later, the Metropolitan District locomotives could have been enclosed, it is likely that an open footplate was preferred so that there should be no restriction on the driver's view ahead. However, standing on the open footplate, the crew were subjected to the same smoke-filled atmosphere as their passengers. The latter frequently 'wrote to *The Times*' on the subject. On one occasion at Gower Street station (later Euston), several railwaymen were overcome by the fumes. The Board of Trade instituted an inquiry into the extent and effects of the fumes in the tunnels. The Metropolitan management argued that the atmosphere was of benefit to the health of passengers and that Great Portland Street station, frequently one of the most fume-filled locations, was used as a sanatorium by those suffering from bronchial complaints.

The first semaphore signals on the Metropolitan had two arms on the same axis. One was operated by the signalman in advance and the other by the local signalman. In a way this anticipated the arrangement whereby the Distant signal for the box in advance was mounted below the Home signal at a station and 'slotted' so that it would not move to 'off' unless the Home signal mounted above it had been cleared. There was no electrical connection in the form of a telegraph by which the signalmen could exchange messages. Despite its simplicity the system was mechanically imperfect because at many of the locations the wire from the box in advance was so long, and had to pass round so many curves, that the frictional resistance was too much for a signalman's muscles. Eventually the block telegraph was adopted and the arrangement of Starter, Distant and Home signals, similar to that of the other railways, was also put in place.

To assist drivers in distinguishing one set of signals from another at complicated track locations, some railways fixed a black or white circle at the end of those semaphore arms that applied to secondary lines, such as relief and goods lines. There were many other types of signal arms governing movements, particularly at busy stations; these included 'shunt back' and 'calling on' signals, whose authority to move was governed very much by local operating rules that needed to be understood by all drivers. Some railways distinguished one signal from another on a gantry of many signals by painting on the semaphore arm the name of the route to which it referred; this is also an example of a difference between night and day information provided to a driver.

AUDIBLE SIGNALS

When it was introduced, the 'steam trumpet' – ie whistle – enabled the driver of a locomotive to warn of its approach, and eventually to provide a means whereby a driver could communicate with the brakemen and guards and with signalmen and lineside staff. Each railway had a code of whistle signals. Failure to give the correct signals or to respond correctly to a signal was the cause of a number of accidents. A typical example might occur when a goods train had to set back into a siding in order to leave the main line clear for a following train. On one occasion when a driver attempted to reverse his train back into a siding he realised that the guard had left his van's brakes on. The guard was standing beside the trailing points holding them over so that the train could back into the siding. To save having to walk the length of his train after it been set back, he had changed the red tail light to white before leaving his van. Meanwhile the driver started to give short blasts on the whistle to attract the guard's attention. The signalman had already accepted an express and was waiting for the goods engine's whistle, which would tell him that the train was in the siding. He heard the whistling and, looking down the line, saw the white light of the guard's van. He assumed that the line was clear and 'pulled off' all his signals for the express, which then crashed into the goods train, half of which was still on the main line. The guard contributed to the accident by changing the tail light to white too soon and the signalman by responding to the wrong whistle signal.

In the years before continuous brakes, whistle signals played an important role in the handling of trains on the Lickey incline on the Birmingham to Bristol line. A southbound train had to approach the top of the incline slowly, and its driver had to bring it to a stop at a white post that marked the point at which the incline started and to whistle once to summon the special incline brakeman. Once the train had stopped, the whistle was sounded three times to ensure that the train's guards and brakemen had applied the brakes. The special brakeman then took over command of the train and, when he was satisfied that sufficient braking power was available, blew his whistle once. The driver then opened the regulator just enough to get the train moving. When the brakeman in charge blew his whistle twice, the driver shut off steam and the train coasted down the hill. If the speed was too high, three whistles ordered all brakes along the train to be applied, including those on the engine's tender under the control of the fireman. Throughout this procedure, intended to limit the speed to 20mph, the driver was no longer in command of his train. For the majority of the passengers, ignorance was bliss. However, for those who knew something about railways the descent must have been faced with trepidation.

'LOCK AND BLOCK'

For the first two or three decades of the steam railway, incidents and accidents were more often than not the result of failures of equipment – broken axles and wheels, fractured springs and burst pipes. By the 1860s equipment had become more reliable and the causes of accidents came more from human failures. Drivers, firemen and guards would 'cut corners' in order to keep the trains moving. Drivers might 'take a chance' that a signal would be clear and continue at speed. However, in many of the cases where 'human error' was recorded as the cause of an accident, it was the lack of equipment needed to prevent errors being made in the first place.

Between 1842 and 1889 the Board of Trade endeavoured to encourage the adoption of safety equipment, such as continuous brakes and the block telegraph to keep trains apart, as well as the means whereby a passenger in emergency could alert the driver. Some companies continued to avoid spending money on important adjuncts to the safe operation of trains. Many of the incidents and disasters with which enginemen were involved were the result of what the Board of Trade referred to as 'lack of accommodation'. This was nothing to do with the provision of premises in which enginemen could sign on, take refreshment or rest – it related to the fact that stations and sidings and their trackwork had not kept in step with the increasing volume of traffic and length of trains. For example, sidings and platforms were often too short. Such deficiencies directly affected the work of the driver who could, for example, find that he had to take charge of an excursion train consisting of far more than the usual number of carriages, with insufficient brake power and too long to fit into a siding. Excursion trains were often 'shoehorned' into the timetable, thus providing a potential for accidents because of the train's out-of-the-ordinary operation. There was always the chance that a train would arrive unexpectedly and surprise station staff and signalmen, and even platelayers who had removed a length of rails.

In the 1860s and '70s, with increased traffic and speeds compared with earlier decades, the number of accidents reached an unacceptable level. The two principal technical journals, *The Engineer* and *Engineering*, continued to 'hammer home' the need for greater safety. Something had to be done. But what and by whom? Apart from the technicalities involved, the companies, in general, resented being dictated to by the Board of Trade. This attitude to safety on the part of many of the railway companies persisted until the Regulation of Railways Act of 1889 forced their hands. From then on continuous brakes, passenger communication equipment, absolute block signalling and the interlocking of signals and points became mandatory, known as 'lock and block'. Following a number of instances when, had there been some means of communicating with the driver, an incident or accident might have been avoided, a number of systems were proposed.

The early communication systems used to alert the driver usually comprised a cord that extended from carriage to carriage. When pulled either by the guard or by a passenger, it operated a gong or a whistle on the locomotive to warn the driver that something was wrong. There were two major problems with the system. In the first place, it was mechanically unreliable – the cord might be incorrectly connected so that there was considerable slack, or in wet weather it might shrink and sound the alarm. A driver therefore had to exercise careful judgement when responding to

the alarm. In the second place, the operating rules often stipulated that a train should not be stopped on a bridge or in a tunnel. The inquiry into the circumstances of a fire in a Pullman car of the Midland Railway in October 1882 highlighted the fact the driver of the train did not immediately make an emergency brake application. The operating rules stipulated that when the communication alarm sounded the driver had to look back and survey his train; if he could not see anything that might indicate the need to make an immediate emergency stop, he should keep the train moving until it reached the next signal box and was within the protection of its signals. The Midland train could have been stopped by its continuous vacuum brakes within 300 yards, but it was not stopped for another 1,000 yards, by which time the fire had proved fatal to one of the passengers.

Without continuous brakes under the control of the driver, and with no means of communicating with the guard or brakemen other than using the whistle to 'call for brakes', the footplate crew attending to the locomotive and the view ahead might be unaware of trouble with the train. On the Great Western, for example, a 'travelling porter' sat in a small enclosure mounted on the back of the tender. From this exposed position he was required to watch for signals from the guard or brakemen or for trouble developing with one of the carriages. The enclosure was similar in shape to the semi-enclosed seats provided for doorkeepers stationed in large draughty hallways.

On the LB&SCR Stroudley and Rusbridge developed their passenger communication system. This was an early example of the application of electricity on a train. A bell was mounted in the cab close to the driver's left ear. If an alarmed or nervous passenger wished the train to stop, the driver would hear a continuous ringing of the bell. The guards could also use the system to signal the driver.

ROUTE AND SIGNAL KNOWLEDGE

Sometimes comment was made about the massive arrays of signals on the approach to large junctions and stations. Laymen questioned the ability of a driver to know what they meant. Again, reliance was placed upon a driver's route and signal knowledge. The L&YR had, perhaps, the greatest number of signals per mile, and the NER was reputed to provide a signal for every possible route and movement as well as providing 'shunt ahead' arms below most of the home signals at busy locations, such as Newcastle. The huge array of signals at the approach to Waterloo station at the end of the 19th century was another example of the need for the inquiring layman to count from left to right and relate a particular signal to a particular track or route, whereas drivers soon became accustomed to the display of arms and lights that soared above London's skyline. In each direction there were more than 20 semaphores and, at night, lamps that had to be interpreted correctly. In the thick coal-smoke fogs of the past there could be a sighting problem.

In the UK the majority of signals at a junction or where a number of lines diverged were to the 'geographical' arrangement – that is, for each route ahead there was a 'doll' (post) with a semaphore arm. The height of each signal related to the importance or relative speed allowed over the route. The main-line signal would thus be the tallest. Sometimes corresponding semaphore Distants were also provided. An alternative arrangement, much favoured because of its simplicity, was that of mounting all the semaphore arms on one post. The Board of Trade inspectors of new signalling works always insisted that if signal arms had to be mounted one above the other on a single post, the uppermost should apply to the first line branching to the left and the others, in downward order, to the other directions, with the lowest signal applying to the route on the extreme right. Eventually, the railway inspectors outlawed the multiple-arms-on-one-post system and insisted that the 'geographical' layout be used. However, it was still permitted for use in yards and where speeds were low. For some reason or other, justifiable or not, the Metropolitan did the opposite and arranged for the uppermost arm to apply to the line on the right. Under pressure from the inspectors the single-post arrays were replaced, wherever there was room, by 'geographically' arranged arms on individual posts.

The 'geographically' arranged junction signals consisting of more than three dolls, and where there were a number of tracks each with its own set of junction signals, emphasised the need for route knowledge on the part of all drivers. That was one reason why 'pilot' drivers had to be used if a train was diverted on to a route for which its driver did not have the necessary route knowledge. Otherwise the regular driver might be confronted with an unfamiliar array of signal arms and lights and be uncertain as to which applied to which route ahead. Even experienced drivers became confused, particularly at complex terminal locations, and responded to a 'go ahead' signal that was not intended for them. Again, expectation was a trap waiting to be sprung.

Although by the end of the 19th century agreement had been reached amongst the many different railway companies over the best shapes, lights and arrangements of multiple signal clusters, there continued to be anomalies. Too many signals were grouped and positioned to suit the signal engineers, and did not always take into account the visual task of a driver. Examples to be found on the L&SWR and the LB&SCR included Home signals for tracks paired by direction that were mounted together to one side of the outermost track. Such ambiguous arrangements were contrary to the usual signal practice; reliance was placed on a driver's route knowledge to ensure that he did not mistake one signal for the other by assuming that he was approaching a junction signal referring to just one particular track and not two. Drivers and 'passed firemen' had to learn all aspects of a route, such as speed restrictions and trap points as well as the location of all signals (see the comments on the Norton Fitzwarren accident in Chapter 6).

One could not fail to notice that many semaphore signal blades in Britain were so covered with dirt and grime that their original bright colours of red or yellow were obscured. The original intention that the colours would serve to distinguish one type of signal from another was compromised by the atmosphere and the lack of staff to keep them clean. Once again, safety depended on experience.

REINFORCING THE VIEW AHEAD

An unfortunate fact of engine driving life was the ever-present danger of an adverse signal being missed. During the 19th century a number of in-cab signalling systems were devised, tested and installed to provide a visual or aural warning to the driver of an adverse signal. As early as 1840, on the London & Birmingham Railway,

A typical two-arm station signal of the South Eastern Railway, c1880. These were primarily used as block signals and did not necessarily indicate whether or not a train could proceed through any of the turnouts or crossovers within the station area. *Author*

Bury's mechanical system of in-cab signalling was tried. A whistle in the cab was sounded if a train passed a signal at danger. From the mid-19th century onward numerous ideas were put forward that would warn and alert the driver and, in some cases, intervene in his actions. The simplest, perhaps, was a semaphore blade that, when in the 'on' position, stood across the track and would be struck by the locomotive. Until the advent of electrical means of communicating with a train, the majority of warning systems comprised an arm that, when raised in concert with an adverse signal, would strike a corresponding arm on the engine that would sound a warning on a whistle.

In 1857, following an accident on the LB&SCR, the coroner asked the driver involved if he knew anything about a system of automatic train control. Such a system had been described in Dickens's *Household Words*. Apparently the driver had never heard of such a device and neither had the Board of Trade inspector nor the company's solicitor. It is interesting to note that the term 'automatic train control' (ATC) was used and would be continued to be applied to systems, such as that of the GWR in 1906. However, they were not strictly 'automatic control' in the true meaning; today we would expect an 'automatic train control system' to exercise full and continuous control and not just act as an intermittent safety device.

Another example of early in-cab signalling was John Hardy's mechanical system of 1876 on the North Eastern. This comprised pendant levers at each corner of a locomotive's buffer beam, which were connected to the whistle. When a Distant signal was 'on', an arm stood vertically at the side of the rail, which would connect with the arm on the engine and thus sound the whistle. An alternative was the use of a ramp that was raised when a signal was 'on'. A lever below the locomotive would then be moved as it passed over the ramp, thereby operating a steam whistle in the cab. In the early 1870s both the London, Chatham & Dover Railway (LC&DR) and the LB&SCR tried this method of providing an in-cab warning signal. When air brakes came into use such methods could be used to apply the brakes automatically.

By 1874 Lartigue had anticipated the GWR ATC and developed an electrically operated cab signalling system for the railways of France. Essentially, this system comprised a wire brush positioned below each locomotive and a conducting ramp, the 'crocodile', in the 'four foot'. If the associated signal was clear, the ramp was energised and an indicator in the cab showed 'all clear'. If the ramp was not energised, a warning sound and indication was given. This system was further developed and incorporated with the Flaman recording and vigilance system ('l'Espion', or 'the spy'). This provided a record at the end of each journey from which the driver's attention to speed restrictions and his acknowledgement of every warning signal could be checked. In the years of the steam locomotive in France the maximum allowable speed was 120kmph, and this was strictly enforced, which is why a driver had to endeavour to operate within the limit at a near constant speed in order to keep to time, despite any adverse gradients.

Vincent Raven of the North Eastern Railway started to study ways of providing the driver with an indication in the cab of whether a signal was 'on' or 'off'. His first warning apparatus of 1894 consisted of a mechanism with an arm, similar to that in the Hardy system. When the adjacent signal was in the 'on' position the arm stood vertically so that it would be struck by a pendulum lever on the engine, which would cause the lever to open a valve in a steam pipe to the whistle. This all-mechanical system worked reasonably well. A collision in 1894 at Wiske Moor on the NER between an express passenger train and a freight train prompted the railway to order the installation of the Raven apparatus and it was fitted to many express and fast freight locomotives. A number of improvements were made over the years including, on Westinghouse brake-fitted engines, the provision of a limited application of the brakes. However, this system was not 'failsafe' because, should the warning whistle become blocked or part of the trackside mechanism fail, a driver could be led into assuming 'all clear' when in fact he had gone past an adverse signal.

Raven went on to develop an electrical version that not only gave, on an indicating panel in the cab, the aspect of the signal ahead, but also, at the approach to a junction, the route that had been set. Although the cab signalling system worked satisfactorily, like the air brake on the NER it survived for only a few years after the 'Grouping' of 1923.

3
BRITISH FOOTPLATES OF THE 19TH CENTURY

The evolution of the steam locomotive between 1830 and 1840 took it from the 'Planet'-type 0-2-2 to the early six-coupled types and the provision of a more substantial footplate, albeit still an open platform with minimal protection for the crew from the elements or from being thrown off. Hackworth's 0-6-0s for the Stockton & Darlington Railway, with vertical cylinders driving the coupled wheels through a jackshaft, positioned the enginemen on a small raised platform that was an extension of the running boards. At the corners of the 'footplate' – and only at the corners – were elegant railings whose origins may have been on the balconies of the Regency terraces of Bath and Brighton. The regulator and the valve gear controls were set between the cylinders.

MECHANICAL CONVENIENCE

The horseman, the coachman and the master of a steamship controlled their vehicle from a position that commanded a reasonable view ahead. In contrast, by the 1840s the driver of a locomotive was sharing the view ahead with steam, smoke and parts of the machine. The control position of the steam locomotive evolved during the first two decades of the steam railway from a number of prototype designs. As noted, some of the earlier types of locomotive, particularly those with a single return-flue boiler, were designed so that, in the normal direction of running, the firedoor end led. That was also the chimney end. Once the basic Stephenson arrangement of chimney at one end and firedoor at the other became the standard,

designers concentrated levers and indicators around the firedoor. Both driver and firemen could thus work together and keep an eye on the machinery, as well as looking ahead along the track.

REGULATOR

The handles and levers of the primary control, the regulator, came in various shapes and direction of movement. An embryonic control stereotype that emerged with the development of the stationary steam engine was the direction of rotation arranged for handle or wheel, which was clockwise to close. Right-handed people prefer to close or screw down a valve, tap or bottle-top with a clockwise rotation of the wrist because that provides the greater strength. Therefore the usual direction of movement for the regulator handle was anti-clockwise to open. This is not to suggest that a regulator was necessarily more difficult to close than to open. On the narrow footplates of Victorian locomotives the regulator could be reached without too much stretching. However, room had to be found in which the fireman could swing his shovel. As the back-to-back dimension between the driving wheels was fixed at 4ft 5in, that limited the footplate width of a typical narrow-firebox four- or six-coupled locomotive to not much over 4 feet.

The designers of the early locomotives tended to keep things as simple as possible. Because one of the best positions for the throttle valve was high up in the boiler, a rod could be used to extend the valve spindle to the footplate. Therefore, for the majority of British engines and for many in other countries the regulator handle axis was on the centre of the backhead. An alternative to a rotating shaft was a pull-push rod attached to a long lever having its fulcrum to one side of the gland through which the rod passed. Some of the early locomotives had regulator valves of the plug type. To move the plug in and out, the regulator handle moved over a quadrant that was set at an angle to the shaft, so that when it was rotated anti-clockwise it pulled the plug off its seating.

REVERSING LEVER

The other important control was the reversing lever. In about 1835, with the invention of the eccentric-driven valve gear, came the single lever for controlling the direction of running. On the majority of the illustrations and drawings of the time the reversing lever is positioned on the right-hand side of the footplate; as mentioned earlier, one reason for this choice between sides could have been the influence of the coachman's preferred side.

In 1841 William Williams devised a link motion to provide a variable cut-off that enabled the driver to 'link up', thereby taking full advantage of steam expansion in the cylinders and economising on fuel and water. This 'milestone' improvement in efficiency of working was refined by Robert Stephenson and thereafter took his name and was referred to as the Stephenson Link Motion. Gooch, Allan and others also developed variable cut-off gears. The cut-off control was combined with that for reversing.

All locomotives supplied by Robert Stephenson & Co in the 1840s to Belgium, France and Germany had right-hand drive – that is, the reversing lever was on the right. In the 19th century, under British influence, the driver's controls on indigenous French locomotives were usually positioned on the right-hand side of the footplate and would remain on that side, for new construction, until the last decade of the century. Positioning the large reversing lever on the right suited the majority of drivers because most would have been right-handed. The stance and position of the hands on a vertical lever to the right of the footplate, pulled or pushed by a right-hand-preferring driver, are more natural than if the lever was over on the left side.

Until the screw-type reversing gear control was introduced a driver had to take care when adjusting the cut-off. With some types of valve gear the long lever could suddenly and violently move the moment the catch was released. On many types of locomotives fitted with slide valves the driver had to close the regulator in order to remove the steam pressure from the back of the valves before attempting to alter the cut-off. Some drivers preferred after starting to leave the reversing lever where it was and control power with the regulator.

INJECTORS

Until the Giffard steam-powered feedwater injector was perfected for locomotive use in the 1850s, the boiler could only be supplied with water when the engine was moving. A feed pump driven directly off one of the crossheads pumped water from the tender and into the boiler. If the water level of an engine at the head of a train in a station or in a siding was seen to be too low, it might have to be uncoupled and solemnly moved back and forth in order to operate its feed pump. Alternatively, the driver could position the engine against the buffer stops, oil the rails and let its driving wheels spin, thereby operating the feed pump. Eventually most engines had two injectors and their controls were an addition to the total number on the footplate.

COKE

The pioneer designers of locomotives were not only without precedents to guide them, but as they themselves often did the driving and endured the elements, they considered that others could do the same. The first generation of steam locomotives burned coke; this produced lethal fumes that, if trapped inside a shelter or cab, could prove fatal to the crew. However, even after coal replaced coke and there was less danger from lethal gases, and speeds of 50mph were common, designers gave little thought to protecting the driver and fireman from the elements, although some engines had a small vertical screen to give protection from the rush of air, precipitation and smoke.

A VERY DANGEROUS PLACE

This tradition of having only sparse shelter for the crew persisted well into the 20th century, particularly in the UK. Engine crews were expected to face the fury of a snowstorm and freezing temperatures without complaining. In addition, they had to accept, and continued to do so, that their working place was a very dangerous one. They stood or sat close to white-hot coals and to hot pipework with many connections through which passed steam at a lethally high temperature. If the steam locomotive was to be reinvented today, both the safety authorities and the unions might have rather strong objections to its use. Did the drivers and firemen complain about their spartan and sometimes dangerous working environment? It is hard to find any evidence, and what exists is countered by the general acceptance of the conditions, together with a great pride in their calling.

CLOTHING

A fact of engine driving and firing life in the 19th century, and to some extent in the next, was the unsuitable clothing worn by the enginemen. They had, of course, to find their own working clothes. These were usually made of coarse cloth and similar to those worn by those who attended the stationary steam engines. When the Sheffield, Ashton-Under-Lyne & Manchester Railway opened in 1840 the enginemen, together with guards and pointsmen, were provided with double-breasted frock coats with red piping and glazed hats. This consideration on the part of the management did not last because a year later uniformed employees had to provide their own working clothes. In general, there were few examples of specialised protective clothing for workers. What there were usually consisted of a heavy canvas apron or the leather apron of the type worn by a blacksmith. Throughout the years of the steam locomotive there were occasions when the footplate was suddenly engulfed by steam and flames; when that happened the enginemen had to try to open the blower valve or abandon the footplate.

On the open footplate the enginemen had to suffer extremes of temperature. The fireman in particular was exposed to the heat of the fire when firing, but otherwise suffered the cold blast of air flowing across the footplate. A feature of the British weather in the latter half of the 19th century and during the first decade of the 20th was severe winter snowstorms. There were numerous occasions when trains had broken down in snow or were stuck fast in a snowdrift when the fireman was required to go forward along the line in order to summon assistance or report the whereabouts of the train to the nearest signalman. As soon as the fireman stepped down from the footplate and into the snow he was subjected to a sudden and severe change in temperature.

Passenger injuries and fatalities due to accidents were invariably reported in gory detail by the newspapers, but the appalling number of railwaymen killed and maimed each year received far less attention from the general public. There was no comprehensive legislation requiring the provision of safety guard rails or screens to prevent factory or mineworkers being killed or injured by machinery, and enginemen were no better protected from injury by the machinery of the railway. A driver had to go in among the mechanism of his engine in order to ensure that the various parts would continue to be supplied by oil throughout the forthcoming journey. The space between the underside of the boiler and the mechanism left little room for the driver when he had to 'oil over the top'. If the engine should suddenly move he could be killed as the big end of a connecting rod rose up. Frequently, with the train moving at speed, he may have had to leave the footplate and go forward along the running board to add oil to a bearing.

THE RAILWAY INSPECTORATE

Throughout the 19th century the Railway Inspectorate and the railway companies fought a war of opinions, of arguments and of autocratic attitudes, the last primarily on the part of the railways. The technical journal *The Engineer* did not hesitate to criticise many of the working practices of individual companies that it considered were unsafe. One of its earliest criticisms concerned those occasions when a locomotive had been sent out in order to chase after some wagons that had run away unattended. In the 1870s the Inspectors campaigned vigorously for 'Lock, Block and Brake' – in other words, the interlocking of points and signals, absolute block signalling and continuous brakes under the control of the driver of a train. To some extent their efforts were handicapped by disagreement among themselves over the best way to achieve their aims. They could either try and persuade the railway companies to seek their own solutions to the safety problems and implement them, or they could lobby for legislation through Parliament that would force all companies to implement 'Lock, Block and Brake'. A common response to efforts to persuade the companies to adopt systems that would improve safety was one of 'we know best' and 'we will not be dictated to'.

In the 1870s not only was there an increase in the number of railway lines, but there was also a corresponding increase in the number of trains operating at any one time. The safety systems, or rather the lack of safety systems, that had characterised the ways in which the railways had been operated could no longer apply. Average speeds had increased, together with the weight of trains. Yet the ability to stop quickly still depended

This LC&DR Kirtley 0-4-2 well tank in SE&CR service is fitted with a vacuum brake in addition to the Westinghouse for working ex-SER stock. The vacuum system controls and piping have been 'bolted on' to the side of the cab. Eventually the vacuum control would be positioned alongside that of the Westinghouse brake inside the cab. *Author*

on primitive and uncertain methods of braking. By the end of the 1870s the annual number of accidents and the loss of life had affected public opinion, and in turn Parliament, to such a degree that the efforts of the Inspectors had to be reinforced by legislation.

HOW TO STOP

From the earliest years to modern times, starting a train has been comparatively certain compared with stopping it. Every driver wanted to know with certainty that once he had got his train moving that he would be able to stop it.

George Stephenson devised a self-acting braking system for carriages. The principle was very simple. As soon as the tender brake on the locomotive was applied, the carriages started to close up on each other. This caused the buffers to compress and in turn they applied the brakes through a system of levers. Unfortunately it did not work as smoothly in practice as it did on paper – there was just as much snatching and sliding as with the usual method of stopping. There was also the problem that arose if the driver were to reverse the engine, in order to set the train back – immediately all the brakes went hard on.

As mentioned before, on the early locomotives it was considered that any system of applying brake blocks to the driving wheels might distort them and the track. Until about 1870 the ability to stop a train, particularly in an emergency situation, depended on three things: the driver reversing the engine, the fireman screwing down the tender brake, and the guard and brakesmen (if carried) responding to the driver's call for brakes sounded on the engine whistle. They had to attempt to work in concert in order to stop a train smoothly. This rarely happened. Slowing down was usually accompanied by much snatching of couplings, violent compressing of buffers and the sliding of wheels. A coach or wagon might even become derailed. Throughout the operation the one person who should have been in overall control, the driver, had no part to play, other than to reverse the engine if things got out of hand. However, reversing in an emergency was not necessarily reliable; much depended on speed and the condition of the rail surface. L. Smith provided a succinct description of stopping in an emergency when the only method available was the screw-down wooden brake blocks on the wheels of the tender:

'They came thundering down … to find the distant red! Shut off, screw down the hand brake, whistle! Round the curve and horrors here was the home red too, and the gates across the line.'

From the earliest years it had become customary for the fireman to be responsible for applying the engine's hand-operated brake. This became the start of a tradition that, as will be explained, affected the individual responsibilities of drivers and firemen and the design and location of the control levers of power-operated braking systems. When the Sharp Stewart 0-4-2 well-tanks of the Furness Railway were equipped with the vacuum brake, the ejector and associated piping was mounted not on the driver's side but on the fireman's side, the brake handle being mounted outside the cab. A similar position was to be found on ex-LC&DR Kirtley 0-4-2Ts of the SE&CR adapted to work with vacuum-braked stock.

CONTINUOUS BRAKES

The attempts to devise a system of braking that would take effect simultaneously and smoothly on all the vehicles of a train were numerous. A number of mechanical continuous, but not automatic, braking systems were tried. The Wilkin and Clark chain brake for the NLR and Webb's improved version for the LNWR worked reasonably well, particularly compared. with others. These used the momentum of the train to provide the power needed to apply the brake blocks to the wheels of the carriages. On one of the axles of the brake-van was a flywheel, and by means of a lever the guard could move another wheel against it. This wheel was part of a windless drum around which passed the continuous chain that extended the length of the train and operated the brakes of each carriage. Six carriages was about the limit for effective operation; any additional set of vehicles had to be provided with its own brake-van. As for the passengers, on the Metropolitan for example, they were subjected to much jerking and noise when this type of brake was applied.

Of course the driver had no direct control over the train brakes other than by means of a code of signals given on the locomotive's whistle. So what of the need for the guard or brakemen to attract the attention of the driver? One company's rules required the brake to be fully applied, then immediately released, such action being intended to alert the driver to a problem with the train. Although Webb considered the chain brake to be effective, he developed a vacuum-operated brake system of his own. This, however, was suppressed by Richard Moon, Chairman of the LNWR, for although it would comply with the Board of Trade's requirements for adequate automatic continuous brakes, he was not going to be dictated to by the Board.

However, most of the systems proposed or used were not, using modern terminology, 'failsafe', and, as noted, they were not under the direct control of the driver. In 1874 Captain Tyler of the Board of Trade set out the basic requirements for any system of continuous brake, be it compressed

Vacuum brake ejector and control levers. Eventually the vacuum brake was fitted to the majority of British locomotives, and when the actual ejector part was separately mounted on the side of the smokebox the installation took up less room in the cab. *Author*

hydraulic, air, vacuum, electric or just mechanical. It had to be cheap to construct, be simple in action, readily adjustable, not in need of frequent attention and repair, not liable to get out of order and, most importantly, applied at the will of the engine driver. The last criterion, when met, replaced the long tradition that the brakes of a train were not necessarily completely under the control of the driver.

In 1875 came a milestone in railway safety. This was the Newark Brake Trials organised by the Royal Commission on Railway Accidents to compare different systems of automatic and non-automatic continuous braking. Among the different continuous automatic brakes was that of George Westinghouse. In America in the 1870s he set about developing an automatic and continuous air brake, and in one evolutionary step he advanced the safety of train operating. This gave the American engineer (driver) the advantage, compared with his British counterpart, of being able to effect control of his train by the air-operated brake fitted to every item of rolling stock. Westinghouse's brake addressed the problem facing an engineer when handling a long train over an undulating track. One third of the train might be on a down gradient, the middle portion passing over a hump and the tail on an up gradient. The engineer had to be highly skilled in preventing his train from breaking in two. This situation was analogous to the British driver handling an un-braked loose-coupled train of four-wheel coal wagons over an undulating route.

After the Newark trials some companies adopted the fully automatic vacuum system while others went for the Westinghouse compressed-air brake. Among the 'vacuum' companies, despite the opinions of Moon, was the LNWR. Apparently Westinghouse himself had attempted to persuade Webb to adopt his system. Because the 'persuasion' included a £20,000 'sweetener', the upright and most honest Webb had him 'shown the door'. Had there been a more ethical approach to Webb, the LNWR might have become an 'air brake' line.

When continuous brakes, mechanical or air (pressure or vacuum), were introduced to meet the requirements of the 1878 'Brakes' Act, some companies instructed their drivers to only use the tender handbrake when entering a station in preference to the continuous pressure or vacuum

system. It was revealed at an accident inquiry that on the Great Eastern Railway the custom of the fireman being responsible for braking had not been abandoned. On 28 February 1884, as a train approached the buffer stops in Liverpool Street station, the driver did not apply the air brake but instead relied on the fireman applying the handbrake on the tender. A combination of misjudgement of speed, a slippery rail and a muddled company policy over the use of the brakes resulted in a collision with the buffer stops and injuries to a number of passengers. Only when it was too late did the driver apply the Westinghouse air brake on the train.

The practice on the GER of relying on the tender handbrake to bring a train to a standstill may have been because the company was not convinced that the air brake could be relied upon. This attitude may have been encouraged by the Board of Trade's opinion, published after a number of accidents caused by the then non-automatic brake systems failing, that it was better to forbid the use of the continuous brake for stopping at terminal stations than risk it failing. Drivers were recommended to enter terminals at a speed slow enough to permit a stop using only the handbrakes. Eventually the practice by some railway companies of treating a continuous braking system as a stand-by to be used only in an emergency was abandoned, although there was at least one example on the Midland Railway in the 20th century. The BOT Inspector's report on a severe buffer-stop collision at St Pancras station averred that the train's speed should have been reduced sufficiently and early enough to allow the train to be stopped using only the handbrake on the tender of the engine. Richard Hardy recalls that even as late as 1945 the firemen of suburban tank engines coming into Liverpool Street station would partly apply the handbrake so that it was available for full action if needed.

THE CAB

We tend to generalise and talk about the locomotive 'cab'. When it became practicable to burn coal instead of coke, some protection for the footplate crew from the elements was acceptable. However, for the first 30 or so years the 'cab' was nothing more than a footplate. By the middle of the 19th century the speed of express trains had

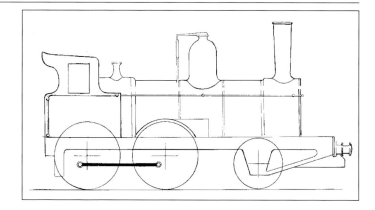

A Blyth & Tyne 2-4-0, c1870: a mixture of elegant and square lines and acknowledgements to the lineaments of the horse-drawn carriage. *Author*

reached a level at which the enginemen required greater protection from rain, snow and ice being hurled into their faces. Each railway company, and those responsible for such protection, had an individual opinion on the need for it. Therefore it would not be for another 30 years or so that a cab with roof and sides was considered essential. As already mentioned, this was at first just a vertical shield or weatherboard at the front of the footplate. Eventually this evolved into the spectacle plate or weatherboard having glass windows through which the driver could keep a lookout ahead without too much rain and snow being hurled at his face and eyes. The next step was to bend the top back to provide a rudimentary roof. A similar evolutionary trend was to merge the sides of the cab with the spectacle plate. The Stirling GNR engines of the late 1860s are a good example of an early attempt to provide side and overhead protection for the crew.

Decade by decade the principal features of the British cab emerged – an overall enclosed roof, front and sides. Side windows, or a shaped cut-out to the side, were usually indicators of 'style' and identified the company. A North Eastern side-window cab was readily identifiable, particularly as the windows were set too low for comfort when compared with, say, those of the GCR and GER. When the L&YR 'Atlantics' first appeared the sides of the cab were dangerously low and had to be modified; the Horwich drawing office had simply copied the cab of a 4-4-0 that had a lower-set footplate. As for side doors, some railways provided them, others thought them unnecessary.

1870 is an approximate year to define the end of the pre-cab era – from then on greater protection was afforded to enginemen. By about 1880 the majority of new-build engines were provided with a cab. Patrick Stirling, in charge of the locomotives of the G&SWR, was another engineer who had some consideration for the well-being of the drivers and firemen. For a further series of 2-2-2s, built at the company's Kilmarnock works in the 1870s, he designed a narrow cab having sides in which there were round 'portholes'. His good intentions were not appreciated by the drivers who complained that they found it difficult to see out. Therefore the side-sheets were cut back at waist level and the roof shortened. This arrangement became a feature of subsequent G&SWR cabs. In general, whenever a cab having an overall roof and adequate sides was provided, some footplatemen were against the idea. As mentioned above, they had a stoic attitude and did not like being over-protected from the elements. At the same time managements were reluctant to provide such protection because they thought it might divert the enginemen's attention from their duties; it also added to the cost of an engine. Irrespective of the extent to which the enginemen were provided with a screen or weatherboard, they were still subjected to the swirling winds that blew across the footplate from all sides.

One cannot easily avoid reaching the conclusion that locomotive design offices considered a cab to be something to occupy whatever space or volume remained after all the other elements of the locomotive had been taken into account. For example, the footplate of an NER 'S' Class 4-6-0 extended back from the firedoor for only 2ft 8in; this meant that the fireman had to stand with one foot on the fallplate between loco and tender when firing.

TANK ENGINES

On some tank engines, designed to spend half their time running backwards, there was often no screen for that direction of operating. Suburban tank engines either had no back to the cab (eg on the Metropolitan) or the driver's view of the track and signals was obscured by the bunker when going astern. Drivers of tank engines being driven backwards traditionally had to operate controls that were arranged for forward running. One example of where a designer had considered such circumstances was the Whitelegg 4-6-4 tank engine of the G&SWR introduced in 1922. With the exception of the reverser, the principal controls of these massive locomotives – regulator, brake valve, whistle and sanding lever – were duplicated. However, the cab provided only a restricted view ahead. A combination of badly positioned signals and the restricted view nearly resulted in a serious accident. When running in reverse and with the firedoor open, the light from the fire was reflected by the windows in the back of the cab. Few draughtsmen appeared to consider how the fireman of a completely enclosed cab on a small tank engine was supposed to manoeuvre a long red-hot fire iron without burning himself or the driver. This is just one of numerous examples of the failing on the part of design offices to consider adequately the real world of the footplate.

Not until the 1950s was greater attention given to the design of the footplate in relation to the crew. Among the few learned papers on the subject was that of F. Rich to the Institution of Locomotive Engineers. He considered that draughtsmen in locomotive design offices should have a sound knowledge and hands-on experience of the 'rough and tumble' of the footplate. Importantly, he includes, as a subject for study, the disposal and preparation of a locomotive. L. A. Summers makes a telling point when he opines that Rich's paper was two or three decades behind the time when it should have been written.

The safety and working conditions of footplatemen were given no more consideration than that given to miners, factory workers or, for that matter, the shed staff. Even today, do the cabs of preserved steam locomotives – with, for example, clusters of very hot pipes close to the driver – conform to the requirements of the Health & Safety Executive? Irrespective of the answer, they still reflect accurately the working conditions of the footplates of the last two centuries.

THE GREAT WESTERN

When Brunel was establishing the broad gauge Great Western Railway as one of the first main lines in the country, the Locomotive Superintendent, Daniel Gooch, ordered 2-2-2s from the locomotive building companies. *Firefly*, a 2-2-2 of 1840, had a 'haycock' firebox on the side of which was mounted a glass water gauge. Its

A typical GWR open footplate, c1850. There are few controls: the regulator is at the top centre of the backhead with the cut-off/reversing lever on the right. Handrails are provided to enable the enginemen to 'top up' the various oiling points when on the move; these remained a feature of GWR engines until the end of the broad gauge in 1892. *Author*

principal features, apart from the large-diameter driving wheels, was the continuous platform or running board on both sides and the positioning of the reversing lever on the right. A handrail was fixed on pillars along the length of the running boards. During the 19th century many GWR locomotives featured railed-in running boards with no handrail fixed to the boiler. This arrangement emphasised that the running boards were an extension of the footplate and that the enginemen were expected to move forward when a train was moving in order to top up the oil reservoirs. Until the development of air and steam sanding systems, firemen had to go along the running board when an engine was moving in order to drop sand by hand. The famous *North Star* retained this feature until it was taken out of service in 1870. The 'Rover' Class engines, apart from a cab and some modernising details, could trace the origins of some of their details back to the Gooch 2-2-2s of 1838, including the distinctive handrails. These engines served until 1892, the last year of the Broad Gauge. The railed-in running board became a very distinguishing feature of Russian steam locomotives, whose running boards in winter became a lethal skating rink.

The 'Caesar' Class engines of 1851 exhibited a small spectacle plate on top of the raised firebox. The question that arises is, why was it so small? It could have been extended to the full width of the firebox. The railings on the outer edge of the running board extended back alongside the footplate. Between the railings and a small side-sheet stood the reversing lever. It was not until the tenure of William Dean (1877-1902) that cabs were included at the drawing board stage.

THE NORTH EASTERN

By 1854, following a succession of mergers, the North Eastern Railway had become a transport monopoly in the North East of England. One result of the formation of what would become one of the largest railway organisations in the country was the acquisition of two principal locomotive designing and construction centres, at Darlington and Gateshead. These, together with the individual design practices of the factories supplying engines, such as Robert Stephenson & Co, Hawthorn and Kitson, resulted in a mixed bag of types and in turn variations in the degree to which the enginemen were protected from the elements.

One of the first attempts in the North East to provide some degree of protection was the weatherboard with two circular glass windows fitted to *Derwent*, an 0-6-0 of the Stockton & Darlington. Once again, it is difficult to understand why the weatherboard was made so narrow and not extended to the full width of the footplate, even though cut-outs would have been needed on each side to accommodate the cylinders. *Derwent* was retired by the NER and placed on a pedestal in Darlington Bank Top station, but its weatherboard may not have been provided when the engine was built in 1854. Among the different types of locomotive that came from the constituent companies were some built by Robert Stephenson & Co. That company's 'Long Boiler' 0-6-0s of the 1840s had only a railing at the sides of the footplate and nothing alongside the boiler.

The Stephenson engines were typical of their time, having the boiler and firebox lagged with

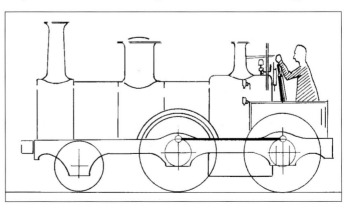

A Hawthorn 2-4-0 of 1852, providing an early example of the spectacle plate and proper sides to the footplate in place of railings. This was the progenitor of the enclosed cab and was intended to provide the crew with some protection from the elements when the engine was moving, but none from vertical precipitation. *Author*

Brougham and *Lowther* of the NER, c1860, provide examples of the first British enclosed footplate, which was not liked by the enginemen even though it was specifically intended to protect them from the harsh operating conditions on the Newcastle-Carlisle line. They considered that, when leaving the warmth of the cab, they might catch a chill! *Author*

wood and an open footplate. Later versions had metal side-sheets in place of railings to prevent the enginemen from falling off the footplate. The type and position of the controls were also typical. The regulator was attached directly to the spindle of the plug valve in the collector pipe below the boiler-mounted dome, and its handle moved in the upper quadrant. In front of it was the valve

This NER Fletcher 2-4-0 of 1875 exhibits the company's unusual shape of cab. Visible is the very tall cut-off/reverser lever and the fine-adjustment handle on the end of the pedestal. *F. Hornby*

lever for the whistle, and the reversing lever, on the right, moved fore and aft between the side-sheet and the side of the firebox. By about 1855 the superintendent of the North Eastern, Edward Fletcher, introduced a weatherboard for his new 0-6-0s, the top edge of which was turned back to provide a narrow overhead shelter if the enginemen stood close up against the firebox. But such consideration for the enginemen was not perpetuated when a further batch was built in 1861 – they had only a very small weatherboard without any form of roof.

The NER, or rather one of its constituents, can be credited with introducing what would eventually become one of the most common types of cab. In 1860 William Bouch ordered two outside-cylinder 4-4-0s, *Brougham* and *Lowther*, especially for operating along the Darlington to Tebay line of the S&D. The line was subjected in winter to heavy snowfalls and strong winds. Bouch took the unusual decision for the time of providing the enginemen with an enclosed side-window cab. In mid-Victorian years such consideration for the well-being of employees was very unusual. But the enginemen objected to being enclosed in a large cab with a roof that even extended back over the tender.

As on other railways, protection for the men on the footplate progressed from weatherboard, to a turned back top to the board, and eventually to the merging of front, sides and roof. At one stage during the time of Bouch's responsibility for S&D locomotives an unusually shaped cab emerged that was neither perpetuated nor copied by other companies. The side-sheets extended both forward and back from the hoop-like shape that provided a roof. Fletcher modified the Bouch shape by extending the roof backward and providing a

'Air' and 'vacuum' brake controls in an **NER** cab. As with other companies, the **NER** had to operate 'vacuum' stock from 'foreign' lines. *Author*

curved cut-out at the sides, the whole having the appearance of a horse-drawn carriage whose hood had been put on backwards.

In the 1870s most new locomotives for the NER had some form of cab and those built in the previous decade were modified to provide protection for the men on the footplate. An example is the 2-4-0 class of 1874 with the unusual name of *Ginx's Babies* (spelled *Jinks* in Maclean's *Locomotives of the NER*), which had an odd-shaped box-like cab with side-sheets extended in front of the spectacle plate. This shape continued to be applied to subsequent classes but with gracefully curved edges.

When Alexander McDonnell succeeded Fletcher in 1883 the very conservatively minded drivers of the NER took exception to some of the changes he made. The Fletcher engines were fitted with an exhaust cock whereby the driver could divert part of the exhaust away from the blastpipe, thereby softening the blast. The enginemen were of the opinion that this resulted in a smooth operation of the engine, and its removal by McDonnell was viewed with great hostility.

Mc Donnell decided that for new construction the controls on the footplate would be moved over to the left side. The enginemen were astounded. Why change? Why not leave things as they were? They had to be persuaded that. when on the left of the footplate. they were not only on the side on which the majority of signals were placed but they were also alongside most of the station platforms. Of course, with the small boilers of the time the view of signals was not too restrictive from the right-hand side of the footplate. One of the objections more than likely came from the firemen, who had to fire left-handed when the driver stood on the left. But this was not to be the end of the left-right argument because T. W. Worsdell, who took over from McDonnell in 1885, reinstated a right-hand control position including the valve for diverting some of the exhaust steam away from the blastpipe.

In his book on North Eastern locomotives, O. S. Nock refers to McDonnell's decision to move the driver's position over to the left. However, he makes no reference to the relationship between the driver's position and that of the majority of signals. Also he rarely discusses the position and type of controls fitted to North Eastern locomotives. This does not come as a surprise because in the early 1950s this writer tried to encourage him to write more about signals in general and to consider the ergonomics of the cab. I referred him to his 1947 book *British Locomotives at Work* in which are appended photographs of the footplate of a number of engine types that would have provided an opportunity for him to comment on their cab fittings. For example, some readers may have questioned why in the photograph of the cab of a 'B17' it had what appeared to be the lid of a fryer from a fish and chip shop mounted in front of the firehole door. He made it clear that he had no particular interest in the subject

One of the first NER classes to have a side-window cab, other than *Brougham* of 1860, was the 'D' of 1880. These two-cylinder compounds had two windows on each side. Wilson Worsdell's 'P' Class had a full double-side-window cab. The proportions of the depth of the windows and the space between their upper edge and the edge of the roof were what would have been expected by an architect. But with a new version of the 'P' Class, Worsdell, or more likely his chief draughtsman, set the windows much lower. All this is, of course, a question of aesthetics, so may not be considered to have a place in the subject of the footplate. However, when applied to the much bigger engines at the end of the century the windows were set far too low, particularly if the driver was standing. Is it reasonable to postulate that when a draughtsman made an error, by making the distance between the top of the windows and the edge of the roof too large, it was not noted and therefore not corrected? Is this yet another example of 'It looks about right'?

LNWR

In the quarter of a century that had passed since the Rainhill Trials, the steam locomotive had developed into a familiar arrangement of the principal components. Ramsbottom, who supervised the design of engines for the London & North Western Railway, provided a series of simple and sturdy engines. Their controls were not complicated and they had weatherboards but no roofs over the footplate. From these early engines evolved a distinctive 'Crewe' look, which was perpetuated by Francis Webb when he succeeded Ramsbottom. The LNWR cab and the controls within it remained to a virtual standard for all classes of engines to the end of the 19th century and on into the 20th. This was in keeping with the rigorous standardisation policy adopted, which was so extensively applied that it is not really necessary to consider the cabs and controls of individual classes of engine.

The distinctive features of the 'Crewe' cab were its austere lines, the only curves being those of the cut-out at the sides. On those where the roof extended back to the end of the side-sheets, the cut-outs were framed by vertical stanchions. The spectacle plate had round portholes. Any uncertainty about the best side on which the driver should stand was resolved early on – the LNWR became a left-hand-drive line. It also had more engines fitted with wheel-and-screw than lever reversing. An interesting example of ergonomics was the direction of rotation adopted for the reversing wheel: to move from mid-gear to full forward gear the wheel was turned anti-clockwise. However, the movement of the weigh shaft of the Allen link motion of one class of tank required the wheel to be turned clockwise for forward running. A driver taking over one of these after having just been driving one with the 'standard' wheel movement had to avoid being confused about which way his engine would move when he opened the regulator.

On those engines fitted with the vacuum brake, the control unit, high on the backhead of the firebox or on the spectacle plate, was in two parts. The left-hand unit carried the brake lever, which was moved anti-clockwise to apply the brakes. This was connected by a rod to the ejector steam valve on the right. The vacuum brake control also simultaneously applied the steam brake on the engine.

The water gauge glass had diagonal black and white stripes as a background; the apparent angle of the stripes depended on the level of the water.

A double-headed **LNWR** express at the end of the 19th century: with tall chimneys and working hard, steam and smoke are not in the eyes of the drivers. *Pendragon*

The top and bottom shut-off cocks were connected to facilitate closing them if the gauge glass broke, a small feature but an important one that not every railway provided. On the larger types of engines the shut-off handle was to the side of the cab. The firedoor, hinged along the top, opened inward, and the degree of opening could be set by a lever and ratchet. The lever was to the left of the firedoor so that, when necessary, the driver could assist the fireman by opening and shutting the door between shovelsful to stop too much air entering. A vertical shield to the left-hand side of the firedoor helped to keep some of the intense heat radiated from the open door off the driver's legs. We have to remember that the width of the average cab was only about 5 feet, so driver and fireman worked close together and the driver could easily reach across to the controls without stretching.

Most LNWR engines had only four instruments in the cab: degree of brake system vacuum, boiler pressure, water-level gauge and carriage warming pressure. The boiler pressure gauge on most Webb engines was mounted on the spectacle plate. If a sight-feed lubricator for the valves and cylinders was fitted it was positioned on the driver's side. The injector control valve wheels and associated piping were on each side of the backhead. Branching off from the right-hand injector valve body was a flexible hose that the fireman could use to spray water on to the coal and around the footplate both to keep down the coal dust and to clean the footplate.

STROUDLEY

When William Stroudley took charge of the locomotives of the LB&SCR he believed that, if they were well made, their drivers would treat them with care and attention. He also believed in the principle of 'one engine, one driver'. Painted on the inside of the cab was the name of the driver. Some of the top-link drivers were contracted at an agreed sum not only to drive but to pay their fireman and cleaners and, most importantly, to pay for their fuel and lubricants. What money remained at the end of the day was theirs. Presumably this scheme was intended to be both an incentive and an economy measure. Few other companies adopted it.

A typical Stroudley cab was left-hand drive.

The crew were provided with a duplex gauge that indicated both boiler and steam chest pressures, a feature that was not usually to be found on the locomotives of other British companies. Some LB&SCR locomotives had screw and others lever control for reversing and adjusting the cut-off. Whether Westinghouse approved or not, air pressure from the braking system was used to assist the operation of the cut-off/reversing control in a number of engine types, notably the 0-4-2 'Gladstone' Class. The footplate of most Stroudley locomotives was no larger or smaller than that of those on other railways; the width was about five feet and the distance between the firedoor and the tender shovel plate was about the same. This meant that when firing the fireman had to stand with one foot on the fallplate.

Throughout the history of the footplate we can find examples of the lack of thought given to the relative heights of the firedoor and the shovelling plate of the tender. One might be higher than the other, thereby making it harder for the fireman to move coal from tender to firebox. There do not appear to be any records of investigations carried out by drawing office staff to determine from practical tests, with a shovel and a heap of coal, exactly how a fireman went about his task. Such simple tests could have provided the ideal heights of both firedoor and shovelling plate relative to the level of the footplate.

On those Brighton locomotives built before 1870 there was only one water gauge, on the fireman's side of the backhead. In addition there were two test cocks on the left for checking the level of the water in the boiler should the gauge have to be closed off.

The 'Grosvenor' Class of 2-2-2s were fitted with a steam brake. The brake lever was on the fireman's side, not on the driver's side as might have been expected. This is where we find another example of tradition exerting an influence because, at the time, responsibility for applying the brake or brakes was usually given to the fireman. The handle of the tender brakes, if fitted, was also usually on the fireman's side. However, there were exceptions such as the 'A' Class 'Terriers'. After the Newark Brake Trials of 1875 Stroudley abandoned the intention to fit the vacuum brake system and instead adopted, as standard for the LB&SCR, the Westinghouse pressure air system. The donkey pump for the brake system was

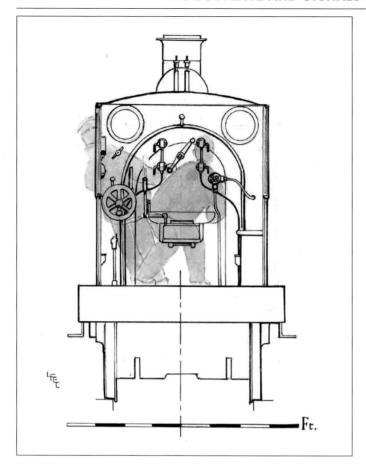

A typical **LB&SCR Stroudley cab**, with the driver on the left and a right-handed fireman on a narrow footplate. *Author*

mounted on the right-side of the engine, providing the 'panting' sound that distinguished a Brighton locomotive from those of the L&SWR and SER whenever it was in mixed company. The control valve and lever for applying the Westinghouse brake of the 'Grosvenor' Class was mounted on the right-hand – fireman's – side of the backhead. But on the 'Gladstone' 0-4-2s, for example, the brake valve lever was mounted on the left and close to the reverser.

How fast?

In the 19th century there were very few speed indicators on vehicles. Perhaps the only widely used one was the taffrail log of merchant ships. On the railway a driver relied on a combination of experience, sensations such as vibrations, and the sound of the wheels passing over the rail joints. Stroudley decided that a more accurate method of determining speed was needed. In 1875 he was granted a patent for a speed indicator. Essentially this was a paddle wheel pump whose shaft was driven by a chord that went round a pulley wheel mounted on the end of the crank axle. The faster the paddle wheel revolved the further it pushed up the water in a vertical glass tube mounted on the inside of the cab. The height of the water could be read against a scale graduated in miles per hour.

The Midland

The apparent indifference to the real world of the footplate by those in drawing offices charged with positioning the controls is highlighted by Tuplin in his *Midland Steam*.

> 'We'd just go into the tunnel when there was bang somewhere up in the front and fire started to blow out through the crack in the

door although the regulator was open. It's a good thing the door was closed, because as it was we were both driven back into the tender and wondered what to do. I thought a bit and decided there was no harm in putting the blower on. So I managed to knock the valve open with the shovel and that pulled the flames down a bit but they were still coming out. I thought about it a bit more and decided that the main steam pipe joint must have gone so that there was not much steam going into the cylinders or out of the blastpipe, but what was passing the regulator was going straight into the smokebox and the blower was not strong enough to pull it all up the chimney. So we had to close the regulator somehow. The old shovel came in useful again and with a few quick stabs I managed to shut the regulator and the cab was clear again.'

The cabs of locomotives on other railways also included controls awkwardly positioned and inaccessible when lethally hot steam and flames engulfed the footplate. Moreover, in general a cab had to be a compromise between being a totally enclosed box with windows, unbearable in summer, or a sparsely sheltered platform exposed to the harsh elements of winter. Overall, particularly in Britain, little room was left for a footplate after all the major components of a locomotive had been fitted within a length limited by the size of the turntables. A small but very important design detail appeared on Joseph Beattie's locomotives for the L&SWR in the 1850s – the footsteps had turned-up edges to prevent an engineman's foot slipping off sideways. This small but important detail was copied by other companies.

THE NORTH BRITISH

Holmes of the North British Railway, when considering the shape of the cab, decided to be different. The traditional British cab side-sheet either had a cut-out or a side window. The cut-out

obviously had to be furthest from the boiler and therefore this position was perpetuated when a side window was used. But on the NBR the window was at the forward end of the cab side-sheet. This suggested that the cab had been mounted the wrong way round.

The locomotives of each of the pre-Grouping companies had their particular characteristics and weaknesses. On the North British one particular item of note was the firedoor; this had a ratchet handle that meant in effect that the fireman had to fire one-handed. He had to push his shovel under the coal pile of the tender, turn and place it on the firedoor plate. Next he had to use one hand to open the ratchet door and instantly thrust with the other a shovelful of coal through the opening. On an engine moving slowly this required a reasonable coordination of the hands. However, when the locomotive was moving at speed he had to keep his feet and his aim true while the fallplate and the tender were moving in different directions.

A MISCELLANY OF CABS

By 1861, if not earlier, L&YR engines, such as Jenkins's 2-4-0s, were left-hand drive. As late as that year in the history of locomotive development there were no brakes on the engine, only on the tender. In the last decade of the century the cabs of some L&YR engines, such as the Aspinall 'Highflyer' 'Atlantics', were equipped with a vertically mounted screw reversing shaft with a wheel on top. On some L&YR engines the steam reversing gear was mounted underneath the driver's seat. Other L&YR cab features were the 'piano-stool' seats. Talking of seats, the sandbox located at each side of the cab in some L&YR 0-6-0s provided a convenient resting place, although it was rather uncomfortable because the lid was fitted with a large knob. However, the ever-resourceful enginemen soon took a heavy hammer and knocked the knob off. Eventually the drawing office took the hint and designed a lid without a knob – another example of the gap between the real world of the footplate and the monastic, far-away calm of the design office.

The 2-2-2 Crampton 'stern wheelers' of the 1850s had the single pair of large driving wheels at the rear. The driving axle was across the back of the firebox and just above the firedoor, and the footplate extended across between the splashers of the driving wheels. The 'Cramptons', when new, had neither a weatherboard nor roof to the footplate, although weatherboards with small porthole windows were eventually fitted to some. In 1867 a Great Eastern 2-4-0 'long boiler' type of 1847 was 'modernised'. Among improvements was a three-sided cab with roof and with portholes at the front.

CONTROL TYPES AND MOVEMENT

By the last quarter of the 19th century the principal elements of the British locomotive cab and its controls were reasonably common to all types of machine. Essentially, they consisted of levers and valves. Levers were usually arranged so that the display-control relationship was easily understood. The principal control, the throttle or regulator, was an 'assumed' valve stereotype, as with the domestic tap, so that the expected movement was anti-clockwise for increased flow, ie power. However, as will be mentioned, in the 20th century, and particularly on left-hand-drive locomotives, the regulator lever might be arranged to move clockwise for opening the throttle. In the 19th century the combined control for reversing and adjusting the cut-off could be a lever. The

A Crampton 'stern wheeler' with a completely exposed footplate, c1860. Spectacle plates were added later to some 'Cramptons'.
Author

A GWR 'Duke' 4-4-0. The cut-off/reverser pedestal and handle take up much of the cab space on the right. *Pendragon*

direction of movement was usually forward for going forward and back for reversing, although there were examples of the opposite movement.

The majority of the alternative wheel-type reverser/cut-off controls were usually arranged so that to go from mid-gear to forward full gear the wheel was turned clockwise. As mentioned, the exceptions, as on the LNWR, were sometimes the cause of confusion and even accidents. According to Tuplin, the first series of 4-4-2s on the GNR had a rotating double-handle reversing control. This was provided with rings shrunk onto the ends of the handles to remind a driver that forward gear was obtained by turning it anti-clockwise. The design office appeared not to be too much bothered about this departure from what had by then become an accepted ergonomic standard whereby rotating a wheel clockwise was analogous to driving a right-hand threaded screw forward. Some designers were of the opinion that it did not

matter which way the reversing wheel had to be turned as long as there was an indicating arrow. Whether or not drivers were expected to look for and distinguish an arrow on a dark footplate is another question. The need to have simple control equipment meant that many levers and valve wheels were in awkward locations. Had human engineering been applied at the time to the Victorian locomotive, grasping, tugging, banging, stretching and bodily contortions would have been part of the descriptive vocabulary.

FRENCH IDEAS

Many of the people who travelled over to the continent of Europe from Britain travelled on the Nord from Calais, then on from Paris by the PLM and the Est. Accustomed to seeing the sparse cabs of British engines, they were not surprised to find a similar lack of protection for the crews of French locomotives. Many British locomotives had very short footplates, but their contemporaries in France were sometimes even smaller.

At the close of the 19th century the Nord

operated some of the fastest trains in Europe. The main line between Paris and Calais included a number of long gradients. In the 1860s the Nord had used 'Crampton' 2-2-2s with completely open footplates. Impressed with Sturrock's 2-4-0s on the Great Northern in England, the Nord acquired similar locomotives. Over the years, train weights increased and had to be matched by increases in the size and therefore power of the engines. The 2-4-0s became the 'Outrance' ('Ultimate') Class, but they were not to be the ultimate – they had to be further developed to meet the demand for more power and faster trains. In their final form they became four-cylinder de Glehn compounds. The next step was to add a bogie.

The cab of a Caledonian Railway 'Dunalastair III' from the turn of the 20th century. The lever on the back of the wheel-arch box is for the extending tablet-catcher. *F. Hornby*

Throughout the Nord's progress from 'Crampton' to the large 4-4-0s, each new class of locomotive acquired a greater degree of protection for the footplate crew. The 'Cramptons' of the 1860s had only a weatherboard, and a roofed cab did not appear on the Nord until the advent of the 4-4-0 version of the 'Outrance'. But even then there was only a short turned-back portion at the top of the weatherboard to keep the rain off the crew. Eventually, in 1896, they were given a proper roofed cab.

FIN DE SIECLE

At the end of the 19th century in the United Kingdom – unlike in North America – there was no virtual standard arrangement of the controls on the footplate. Neither was there a common system of continuous automatic brakes on passenger rolling stock; some railways preferred the vacuum brake, others the air pressure brake. More significantly, perhaps, depending on the reader's interest in lateral matters, was the fact that on some railways the driver's position remained, as it had been at the beginning of the steam railway, on the right of the footplate, while on other railways he stood on the left. Some firemen with the former footplate arrangement fired right-handed and some fired left-handed. If the driver stood on the left and the fireman was right-handed, on a narrow footplate they were in each other's way. As already mentioned, much depended on the width of the footplate. As the majority of British locomotives had a wheel arrangement with a nought at the end – 0-6-0, 4-4-0 – the driving wheel arches took up some of the available room on the footplate.

IDENTIFIABLE CABS

Standardisation by individual companies in the closing years of the 19th century resulted in locomotives, and their cabs in particular, acquiring a readily identifiable appearance related to their ownership. Those who took an interest in the subject could quickly identify from a montage of cab photographs the specific owning companies.

4
BRITISH FOOTPLATES OF THE EARLY 20TH CENTURY

The year 1900 is an arbitrary starting date because by about 1890 the principal lineaments of the British locomotive cab had been settled to a virtual standard for the majority of locomotive types. However, from the turn of the century onward successive types of increasingly larger locomotives would be built. One thing that would not change, in Britain or in the rest of the world, was the common arrangement for most steam locomotives, which positioned the driver behind and not at the front. The steady increase over the years in the girth of boilers would limit a driver's horizontal arc of view. Leaving aside tank engines, there have been few examples of locomotives having the driver's position at the front in the usual direction of running. In Britain the most notable was Bulleid's 'Leader' C-C. In North America the Southern Pacific operated large Mallet-type engines, which, when hauling a train, moved in reverse and towed the tender, thereby keeping the crew at the front. Also, in Italy there were 'reversed' locomotives having the same arrangement as those of the Southern Pacific, and a German high-speed 4-6-4 with an all-over casing with the driver's position in the pointed front.

THE FOOTPLATE CREW

Before considering the development of the British locomotive cab from 1900 onward attention needs to be paid to a very important component – the footplate crew. The basic economic structure of the railways in the United Kingdom in the early part of the 20th century was founded on an adequate supply of good coal and low wages, as well as very few long steep gradients and heavy freight trains. High-quality steam coal was available for the top-link locomotives, yet the coal bill was not a significant part of operating costs. It used to be said that the fare paid by one 1st Class passenger on a train paid for the coal used. A top-link driver in 1900 might earn £120 a year, which might appear to be a reasonably amount. However, account needs to be taken of the – in general – lack of insurance to provide for his family in the event of his death.

Friendly and Provident societies came into being in the 1850s to provide help in the event of a driver or fireman being injured and, should they be killed, to assist their families. The men had to make a weekly contribution to the funds. However, there were wide differences among the railway companies over the extent to which each would subsidise the funds. The Workmen's Compensation Act had come into force in 1895 so that a railway company, for example, had to pay compensation to his dependent family, although in many cases this only amounted to the equivalent of one or, at best, two years' earnings.

Although their standing within the rail hierarchy was equal to that of the signalmen, footplatemen were low down the ladder within society as a whole. Even though their educational standards had improved significantly during the last half of the previous century, drivers were not required to have more than a rudimentary understanding of thermodynamics and mechanics. Of course, many attended the mutual improvement classes in an endeavour to understand as much as they could about operating an engine efficiently. R. H. N. Hardy, in *Steam World*, emphasised that there was no formal instruction given by a company to enable men to qualify for advancement to a higher grade, such as 'passed fireman' to driver. However, he felt that the lack of formal training, other than the enginemen's own mutual improvement classes, made them strong and independently minded and capable of achieving much under difficult circumstances. Probably the French system of training and examinations would have eliminated any that were 'not up to the job'.

L. A. Summers, when writing about the training of drivers and firemen, suggested that the traditional ladder of promotion, starting on the bottom rung as a cleaner, was not the best way in which to train and encourage the career of enginemen. Cleaning a locomotive was a labourer's job. Recruits to the footplate should have had a reasonable understanding of chemistry and physics, and such a requirement would have improved their skills and enabled them to make the best use of a locomotive. Such a policy would have meant adopting a training and promotion regime similar to that of the French.

To enable engine crews to better understand their locomotives, some companies provided 'classroom' assemblies of the braking systems and other equipment, which were used to demonstrate their correct operation. There was at least one example of a complete locomotive cab and all its controls and instruments within a converted coach; this visited engine sheds to enable an instructor to demonstrate the correct procedures to be used when driving and firing an engine. However, there were no 'working' examples of a complete mock-up cab, with sound and movement, comparable with the simulators used for training drivers of road vehicles, masters of ships and pilots of aircraft. Those drivers who moved from steam to electric power could be given the benefit of simulators that replicated all the controls and instruments, sounds, vibrations and movement, as well as a 'view ahead' complete with all signals.

Despite improvements in the working conditions in factories, miners and railwaymen continued to labour at the coalface and the locomotive control face in circumstances no different from those of the previous century. The average footplate to the end of steam remained a filthy and spartan location in which to earn a living. With choking smoke in tunnels, intense noise and the searing heat when the firedoor was open, this was a modern inferno to which was added the very unsociable hours of work.

At the start of the 20th century in Britain, technology was advancing faster than ever before: the telephone had arrived, wireless telegraphy was emerging as an important commercial and military means of communication, the internal combustion engine was about to revolutionise land transport, and within a few years would lead to the conquest of the air. In contrast, the steam locomotive, the trains and the associated safety systems of the railways as a whole were not being advanced to the same degree. The abundance of good steam coal at comparatively low cost and the sometimes limited technical training of both shed staff and enginemen together contributed to the railway companies' reluctance to try anything new; particularly if it meant capital expenditure.

The unbraked 10-ton private owner wagons that made up the majority of freight trains needed only simple types of engine; this was because they were likely to spend half their time lingering in sidings and loop lines, so any devices added to improve their thermal efficiency were wasted. Also, within a circle of cause and effect, locomotive design offices were not encouraged to add components and systems that might improve the efficiency of an engine if their use required specialised training, or, if not used correctly, they provided no significant saving in coal and water. Another factor that weighed against 'gadgets' was the share dividend. A company's directors usually insisted on the cheapest locomotives that would do the work required. Therefore, with only a few exceptions, the steam locomotive for all types of work in Britain was designed to be as simple as possible and to have the simplest methods of control. Since the earliest years of the steam railway in Britain successive generations of enginemen stepped on to the footplate with little expectation that the machinery of which they were in charge would be any more complicated that those that had gone before. From the company directors downward, nearly everyone on the railway figuratively had a sampler on the wall that declaimed 'We have always done it that way. Why change?'.

The two-cylinder 0-6-0 freight engine became the most common type on the railways of Britain. Apart from superheating, its major components, including the cab and its equipment, were hardly changed from those of its mid-Victorian ancestors. Hundreds were employed in hauling freight trains made up of unbraked wagons joined by loose-link couplings. In many ways the driver of a typical freight train in the days of steam had to exercise a greater skill than that of the driver of a train equipped with continuous brakes. The driver could only slow the train and bring it to a stop by using the steam brake on the engine and tender wheels and trust that the guard at the tail end of the train applied the handbrake of the brake-van. When operating a long train over an undulating route the driver and guard had to cooperate to prevent a sudden snatch that could break a coupling. A familiar saying on the railway was 'Anyone can start an engine but it takes a skilled man to stop it.' However, starting the locomotive of a long, heavy, loose-coupled freight train also needed great skill. The driver had to start moving the train slowly so that, progressively, each coupling was stretched out until finally the coupling at the brake-van was taken up and the guard could signal to the driver that all the train was intact.

ACHILLES HEEL

Those who understand the technology have often commented upon the 'Achilles heel' of the British steam locomotive – namely, the ashpan. Too many design offices on too many occasions handicapped both drivers and firemen, particularly the latter, by the restricted dimensions of the ashpan. The traditional British narrow firebox, with the ashpan having to share space with the axle boxes of the driving wheels, was very prone to the build-up of ash to an extent that it obstructed the flow of air to the fire. In turn, a choked ashpan made the fireman's task harder and frustrated the driver. Yet, in many cases, just another six inches added to the height of the boiler centre-line might have provided a less cramped ashpan. It is instructive to study the detail drawings of LNWR locomotives and note how shallow the ashpans were. In his *Locomotive Panorama Volume 1*, E. S. Cox records that disappointing runs with LNWR 4-4-0s and 4-6-0s

were attributed to the interference of the air flow through the firegrate due to the firebox foundation ring being set too closely above the trailing axles or, in the case of the 'Prince of Wales' Class, the middle coupled axles. Not only did the humps in the ashpans, where they passed over the axles, interfere with the air flow, but ash building up over the hump and in the shallow part of the pan could accumulate to choke combustion air towards the end of a long run, so that the effective grate area was reduced. The 'Claughtons' were particularly handicapped by this. When Drummond decided that the L&SWR needed some big 4-6-0s, the results were not what either he or the enginemen had hoped for. Their firemen needed to exercise considerable skill in overcoming the built-in handicap of a constricted ashpan volume; the grate was nearly flat and was set very close to the axleboxes of the second and third coupled wheels.

The extent to which the design of an ashpan 'choked' the air needed for efficient combustion depended, among other things, on the quality of the coal. Some types of coal produced a greater quantity of ash than others. But, irrespective of the coal quality, there was often enough ash to block up the more confined areas of an ashpan. For example, Whitelegg's massive 4-6-4T for the G&SWR had a small ashpan volume relative to the area of the grate. The part that arched over the third driving axle came within a foot of the underside of the firebars, while the part under the back area of the grate provided only about 3 inches of clearance. Both sections were likely to attract a build-up of ash and thereby restrict the air flow. It is possible that Whitelegg accepted the restricted ashpan dimensions because the 4-6-4T would only have to burn coal that produced little ash, and in any event the average run was less than an hour.

Another example of limited ashpan volume, among a number, was to be found under the grate of a North Staffordshire 4-4-2T. The side elevation drawing shows that the bottom of the ashpan was only 18 inches below the firebars. Yet an additional 12 inches could have been provided without interfering with the brake rigging. In contrast, Robinson of the GCR provided comparatively large ashpans, such as that under a 'Sir Sam Fay' 4-6-0. It is difficult to avoid the generalisation that the majority of chief locomotive designers had a rather optimistic approach to ashpan dimensions. In the end, what mattered was the attention given to cleaning ashpans when on shed and the skill that fireman were able to exercise in using the dampers.

Because the progress from cleaner to fireman and eventually to engine driver included, for the first few years, being involved in cleaning away dirt-encrusted grease and hot ash, the enginemen accepted that their lot was a filthy one. They also, apparently, were resigned to the filth and the arduous and hazardous conditions of the engine sheds. In the 19th century the sand boxes were usually positioned on the running board. In that location they could be reached when the engine was moving should it be necessary to unblock damp sand in one of the pipes. In the 20th century designers continued to arrange the sand boxes on the running board, and one of a fireman's tasks when an engine was being prepared for service was to carry numerous buckets of sand and refill the sand boxes. Of course the sand boxes could have been on top of the boiler, the position usually adopted in other countries. On top of the boiler, the sand was less likely to get damp.

One foreman/driver, Charles Meacher, in his *LNER Footplate Memories*, was scathing in his criticism of the way 20th-century CMEs could not bring themselves to add an extra 'lump', ie a sand dome, on top of the boiler and the means in engine sheds for replenishing the sand from an overhead hopper. But the provision of overhead sand hoppers at every shed, as with other helpful devices, was not always viewed with favour by the management. Once again, why change? It was part of the fireman's job to lug buckets of sand up onto the running board and part of the driver's job to ensure that none of the spilled sand remained in those parts were it was not wanted. However, there was at least one example of a boiler-top 'saddle'-mounted sand box. This was on Churchward's No 2601 of the GWR in 1899, one of the 4-6-0 'Krugers'. Carrying a bucket of sand, the fireman had to climb up the side of the boiler, using the footsteps provided, to fill the sand box, an operation that may not have been viewed with much pleasure. Attending to the sand boxes on a Bulleid 'Pacific', with its smooth sides and no running boards, imposed a very different set of conditions for filling the sand boxes..

Another helpful device was an ash discharge chute from the bottom of the smokebox. This avoided the need at the end of a run to laboriously and awkwardly shovel out the ash, a particularly onerous task in wind and rain. However, once again such an obvious way of disposing of the contents of a smokebox was frowned upon because gadgets in that area, including adjustable blastpipe tops, were subjected to a set of arduous conditions in which a door, for example, might warp and not close properly after use.

GWR CABS IN THE 20TH CENTURY

As already mentioned, the Great Western Railway retained its spartan footplate and cab for all its engines, from the smallest to the largest; the latter included the 'Saints' and 'Stars'.

The standard large engine cab of the GWR was little different in detail from those of the late 19th century. The majority were very short fore and aft. Was all this the result of tradition taking precedence over common sense? To be fair, turntable length did not keep pace with locomotive size increases so that, in turn, there was often a limit to the dimensions of the footplate. There were no side doors, except for tank engines. Why a fireman, for example, was less likely to fall off the footplate of a 'Castle' Class loco than off a tank engine is not clear. As mentioned, right-hand drive was retained to the end of steam at Swindon. The regulator, which extended across the right-hand lower quadrant arc, was moved in the traditional movement of anticlockwise to open. Drivers had to share what space was available with the large pedestal frame for the screw reversing gear and its twin-handled control. They had to adopt a look-out stance requiring the spine to be curved (the '29' bend). Interestingly, the 'Castle' Class 4-6-0s, derived from the 'Star' Class, had the reversing pedestal mounted alongside the firebox so that the control handles did not project back as far as the edge of the footplate, as in the 'Stars'. Why a similar arrangement was not used in the first place may have been because the reversing gear of the 'Stars' required more human muscle power than that of the 'Castles'. Tuplin, for one, opined that a driver could exert more effort when standing in the plane of the handles. This suggests that it could be a reason why so many other types of locomotives,

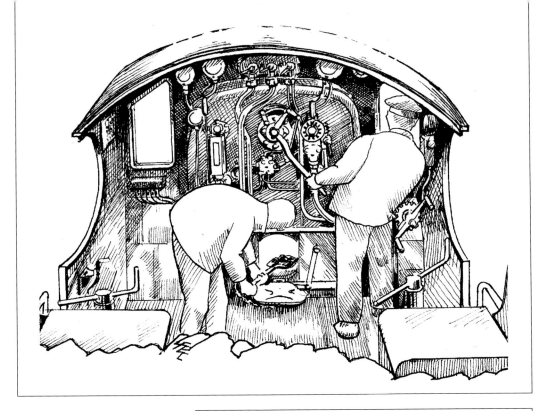

Above The cab of a GWR 'Star'
Class 4-6-0. The cut-off/reverser
pedestal (right) dominated the
footplate and imposed a
particular stance on the part of
the driver. According to the
GWR's regulations, drivers were
not expected to lean out of the
side of the cab. *Author*

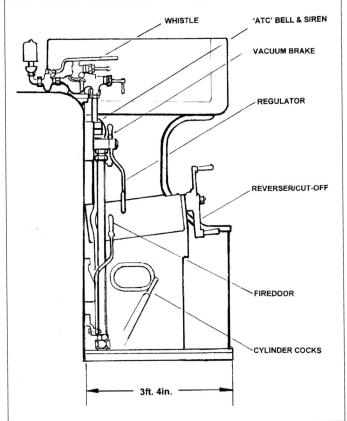

WHISTLE

'ATC' BELL & SIREN

VACUUM BRAKE

REGULATOR

REVERSER/CUT-OFF

FIREDOOR

CYLINDER COCKS

3ft. 4in.

Right The principal controls in
the cab of a Churchward 'Star'.
Author

not just on the GWR, had the reversing handles or wheel brought back to the edge of the footplate.

The solitary GWR 4-6-2, *The Great Bear*, was not given preferential treatment when it came to the design of the footplate and cab; it was a typical GWR size and therefore, aesthetically, not really appropriate. The reverser/cut-off pedestal projected so far back that the driver had to stand on the fallplate to turn the handle.

Was the 1-foot increase in length of the footplate of a 'Castle', compared with the 3ft 6in of a 'Star', provided to give room for the large brake cylinder and not necessarily to improve the cab for the benefit of the crew? One factor that had an influence on GWR cab design was a requirement that the driver and fireman should not have to lean out over the side when looking ahead, as evidenced by the absence of the narrow vertical glass windscreen adopted by other companies. With the exception of possibly only one, none of the locomotives designed at Wolverhampton or Swindon was provided with a side-window cab.

The GWR Automatic Train Control (ATC) apparatus, mounted close to the driver's ear, was the most important 'instrument' in the cab. The ringing of the bell as each clear Distant signal was passed was a most reassuring sound, especially when trying to keep to time in a dense fog.

In 1905 the GWR acquired a French four-cylinder De Glehn Compound. Among its features was a variable blastpipe orifice that was under the control of the driver. This introduced a rather un-British complication to the controls, although Bowen Cooke's 4-6-2Ts of 1910 were fitted with a variable blastpipe as in some contemporary French engines. It may have been the intention to fit an adjustable blastpipe to other classes of LNWR engines; at the time the designer was of the opinion that such a device required considerable skill on the part of a driver in its correct use in order to effect the best economy of working. Also in that year, a simple, uncomplicated, variable-area blastpipe was tried on a GWR 4-6-0. This was the 'jumper top' type, the operation of which was automatic and therefore required no controls in the cab; eventually this became a common feature of most GWR engines. In 1918 Drummond of the L&SWR designed the 'P14', the last of his series of 4-6-0s. The variable blastpipe fitted to some of the earlier series, in order to overcome their poor

steaming characteristics, was abandoned for the 'P14s'. Once again human nature had become at odds with technology, because it had been observed that the majority of drivers always set and kept the adjustable blastpipe at its minimum diameter in order to make sure that the boiler would steam properly.

In the cabs of some Edwardian steam locomotives in Britain there was a pyrometer gauge, which indicated the temperature of the steam in the superheater header. Although such information might have been of use when a new locomotive design was being tested, it is doubtful whether, during day-to-day working, many drivers bothered to look at it. It is on record that when one driver was questioned about the pyrometer gauge in his cab, he replied, I've to keep the needle on that mark but I don't know why.'

On the LNWR and into the first decades of the LMS, the side-sheets, roofs and spectacle plates were very much to the Webb pattern of the previous century. Left-hand drive had been the standard at Crewe for the previous 50 years, and the controls and instruments were positioned on the footplate to a standard arrangement that applied to most of the engines designed and built at Crewe. This was not unexpected, because the drawing office, as with those of other companies, followed what had been done before – another example from the pre-ergonomic years of 'that looks about right'. At the same time it must be acknowledged that to keep down costs every railway company endeavoured to have as many as possible of the components needed for an engine to be from a standard range of items. It must also be recognised that there were some individuals in the design departments who had advanced ideas and wanted to see the application of improved thermodynamics and mechanisms. They were, however, often constrained by their superiors, who were opposed to new ideas lest they proved to be too costly and might fail. The higher management at Derby, for example, wanted medium-size, simple engines, so the design offices were required to stick to the 'devil they knew'.

DRAWING OFFICES

D. L. Smith criticised the cabs of the LMS 0-6-0 'Jinty' tanks that were moved on to the former G&SWR lines:

'They were truly terrible, ... lever reverse, ... one gauge glass. The firedoor was an incomprehensible affair of plates and ratchets and chains ... you could not lean out and watch your shunter while handling the regulator ... take two or three steps across the footplate to work this wretched little upright handle.'

Once again the peculiar, or should it be the perverse, hand of the Derby drawing office made the enginemen's task that much more difficult. The earlier examples of the ubiquitous Derby 4F 0-6-0s also had a regulator handle moving in the upper quadrant, which made it difficult for the driver when leaning out to look for signals from the guard or from shunters.

On some Derby-designed locomotives the control valve for train heating was a square stud rather than a wheel or lever as might have been expected. If the necessary spanner was lost, the passengers froze. There may have been two reasons for this: one was that the control could not be confused with that of the injector steam valve wheels, another that Derby had in mind the maxim 'look after the pennies and the pounds will look after themselves'.

This lack of thought on the part of the design staff at Derby about what might happen was not an isolated example. Drawing offices often seemed to go to great lengths to ensure that a steam locomotive cab was as draughty and wet, or as stifling hot, as could be, and provided with numerous projections for imparting injury to the crew. Nevertheless, drivers and firemen adapted to the spartan conditions. After a time, drivers and firemen overcame difficulties and stopped worrying about them. This and adaptability was relied upon by management, who sometimes would not entertain complaints.

An example of a design office making little attempt to improve the working environment of the footplate crew is the Midland series of 0-6-0s. As A. J. Powell tells us in his *Living With London Midland Locomotives*, 'Let no one suppose that Midland engines were fun for the driver.' He emphasises that the cab offered little protection. When running with the damper open, a fine stream of ash from the ashpan was driven by the air flow up through the various gaps at the back of the firebox and into the cab. A shield was mounted

behind the ashpan to entrain a stream of air and thereby keep any heat radiated by the ashpan from reaching the trailing axleboxes. This had the additional effect of forcing ash that had escaped from the front damper up and into the cab. Of course, the ever-resourceful footplatemen devised ways for overcoming this irritating feature by using sacking or even turf to plug the gap. The records do not indicate whether the restriction to the air flow resulted in overheated axleboxes. On Midland passenger locomotives the reversing screw had to be mounted on top of the rear driving wheel splasher and inside a narrow cab. This left nowhere for the driver to sit, except on top of the reverser. However, the design office had anticipated this and provided a narrow wooden board as a rudimentary seat. But it had to serve another purpose, as a cut-off indicator. A short pointer moved along below a slot in the board, and the slot was marked with notches to provide a crude indication of the cut-off setting.

R. H. N. Hardy has written at length on the driving, firing and maintaining of steam locomotives. Writing from hands-on experience of the footplate, he often refers to details of the controls. The reader, I suggest, cannot avoid concluding that the footplate crews about which he wrote had much to contend with because of badly designed cabs and their controls. However, once again, the ability of humans to adapt to circumstances usually overcame footplate deficiencies.

An ever-present hazard was that of a boiler water level gauge glass bursting. Theoretically, balls at the top and the bottom of the glass were supposed to be forced onto a seating by the rush of steam, but this could not be relied upon. When the footplate suddenly became engulfed in scalding steam, one of the crew had to try and shut off the gauge. To make this more difficult on some engines the shut-off cock levers were not connected so that both could be shut off at the same. On locomotives equipped with two water level gauges some drivers shut off one of them before entering a long tunnel; this was done so that in the event of a gauge glass bursting the driver would know which one of the two had failed. Of course, on GWR engines having only one water level gauge there was no need for such information. Dean's 4-6-0 freight engine of 1896 had a lever mounted on the outside of the cab for shutting off the water-gauge, which raises the question of why this seemingly desirable arrangement was not fitted to all GWR locomotives.

To improve the lot of the enginemen when running in reverse at the head of a train, some locomotives were provided with a tender on the front of which was mounted a cab. There does not appear to have been an overall and consistent policy on the subject, even within any particular class of locomotive.

In 1914 the Derby works of the Midland Railway started delivery of a batch of right-hand-drive 2-8-0 locomotives specifically designed for use on the undulating Somerset & Dorset Joint line. Most of the details were to the traditional Derby standards except for the outside cylinders and Walschaerts valve gear. Because the engines would spend a large part of their time operating in reverse, they were given a double cab with one half on the front of the tender. However, once again we have an example of consideration for the well-being of those on the footplate not being appreciated. Drivers and firemen complained that the tender cab made the footplate very draughty when running in reverse – they preferred the traditional tarpaulin sheet tied to the back of the cab roof. In the early 1920s the tender cabs were removed. The 1925 batch of 2-8-0s for the S&D, having larger-diameter boilers, were left-hand drive. Was this because someone very high up had, at last, realised that the majority of signals were on the left of the track? In addition, the majority of platforms were to the left of the track and therefore a driver could better judge his stop when on the left, and also look out for hand and lamp signals from platform staff and the guard before starting.

Another example of Midland design ideas affecting the shape of the footplate came when the newly appointed CME of the LMS, Sir Henry Fowler, examined the excellent Horwich 2-6-0. He imposed a number of Derby standard fittings on Horwich, despite the fact that they were not the best to be had. He also insisted that the standard Midland tender be used even though it was narrower than the cab of the 'Mogul'. Thereafter these useful mixed traffic engines ran with a gap at each side at the back of the cab.

It is unfortunate that, when reviewing decisions taken in the past, the impression might be given that the individuals and organisations concerned acted irresponsibly. Obviously a few did. However, account must be taken of the fact that it is both wrong and at times pointless to try and consider the past in the light of the present. Not only is hindsight a convenient tool for the historian, but the past, as has so often has been quoted, is 'a foreign country'. Decisions taken in a drawing office over design details, such as those that in retrospect seem foolish or unthinking, need to be considered in relation to the total environment of a railway, not only the cost and mechanical limitations but also the people who had to drive, fire and maintain the locomotives. Above all, as mentioned, 'change', to some, was often a frightening word.

NORTH EASTERN CABS

The express passenger locomotives of the Edwardian era in Britain were, at the time, the epitome of power at speed. In brilliant liveries and polished to perfection, they were an important advertisement for the railways. As they swept by, onlookers might have had a fleeting glimpse of the crew on the footplate. Some may have longed to be in their place. But how many were aware of the difficulties imposed on driver and fireman by the design, or lack of design, of the cab and its controls? An example is that of the North Eastern Railway 'Atlantics'. From the outside the cab appeared deceptively commodious. However, once the observer stepped onto the footplate it was seen that the firebox and the controls on the backhead projected back for half the length of the cab. On each side, and rising nearly to the side window sills, was a large box. These boxes took up so much room that the fireman had a space only 2 feet wide by 3ft 6in long in which to stand and swing his shovel.

When the first NER 'Atlantics' came into service the drivers began to complain that they found it difficult to see ahead past the large boiler, presumably when looking out for signals positioned on the left of the track. The cab roof had to be raised. Possibly some of those drivers were among those that had forgotten they had complained when, in 1882, McDonnell had moved the driver's controls over to the left side.

The majority of British side-window cabs had the top line of the windows at about the same height as the top line of the boiler. The cabs of Worsdell and Raven locomotives of the NER, as already noted, had the side windows set too low, which made them awkward to use. They were also, in the opinion of some, aesthetically too low. If the reader considers the dimensions of a Class 'Z' 4-4-2 it will be found that the top line of the side windows is 1ft 3in below the roof edge and 1ft 6in below the top line of the boiler. The average driver's eye point was about 5ft 5in, and that coincided with the top edge of the side windows. The bottom edge of the forward window was at about the same level. The driver could crane sideways to look out through the low-set window or stand looking ahead through the right-hand spectacle window. In any event he had to stand in order to reach the regulator handle.

Tuplin, in his *North Eastern Steam*, did not hesitate to comment on the NER side window arrangement:

'It must be added that although the side-window cab (NER type) was admirable in providing protection from the weather while the engine was standing or running forward, it could be too hot in summer and could be a nuisance at any time of the year when the men had to be continually looking back alongside the train when shunting. To get his head through the opening in either side wall, a full-sized man in the average Worsdell cab had to "duck" and then to reverse his movement to get back to where he could make any necessary readjustments of the controls.'

The side windows of an NER 'S3' ('B16/1'), when compared with the position of those provided for the 'B16/2s' and 'B16/3' rebuilds, emphasised the awkwardly positioned windows of so many NER locomotive cabs. Even some of the Gresley 'K3' 2-6-0s built at Darlington in 1924 were given North Eastern-type low-set side-window cabs. The North Eastern was an 'air brake' line, the controls for which were usually positioned to the left of the reverser handles. The need for inter-company running of passenger stock required the provision of the vacuum brake in addition to the existing air brake, so room had to be found in the cab for the ejector and controls. This was usually between the

The vacuum brake lever (left) and Westinghouse brake lever (right) in the cab of an ex-LC&DR 0-4-4T.
F. Rich

reverser pedestal and the side of the cab. The injector control valves were mounted five feet above the cab floor, making them difficult to reach unless the fireman was tall. So, altogether, any consideration of the relationship between the body dimensions of the average driver and fireman does not appear to have been studied very closely by the drawing office.

GREAT CENTRAL CABS

The Robinson engines of the Great Central were renowned for their shapely and balanced appearance. Considerable care was taken in the proportions and relationships between the major components, such as the chimney, dome and splashers. The lines of the cab were also carefully drawn to blend with the overall outline. Such considerations did not, however, extend to the position and shape of the controls. The reverser/cut-off screw with its two-handled lever took up most of the space on the right-hand side of the cab. The driver stood on that side keeping a good lookout for the signals, the majority of which were over on the left of the track. The regulator was a small lever on the middle of the backhead moving in the lower quadrant. The vacuum brake controls were positioned just below the right-hand spectacle window.

The driver who wrote under the pen-name of 'Toram Beg' did not hesitate to express his opinion of the right-hand driving position on the GCR 'Director' 4-4-0s allocated by the LNER to the engine sheds of the one-time North British system. He commented that:

'Everything within that cab was far better than we had been accustomed to on the former NBR. Here was room to move, with a far more comfortable seat for driver and fireman than on any 4-4-0 on the NBR, a front window almost twice the size of that on the "Scotts" and better and bigger tool-boxes on the tender end. Why, oh why, most of us moaned, did they spoil it all by putting the brake and throttle controls on the right of the cab? This was a major fault.'

'Toram Beg' went on to explain that the ex-NBR drivers, who were accustomed to sitting on the left, relied on certain landmarks to make sure they stopped their train at a precise position to avoid having to make a double stop because part of the train was not at the platform. They were also accustomed to a certain set of angles to 'catch' the Distant signals when running at speed. Furthermore, emergency signals were more likely to be displayed to the left of the track.

As for the detail ergonomics of a 'Director' cab, 'Toram Beg' pointed out that in order to make precise stops, particularly in the wartime blackout, he had to lean out of the cab window. He then found that the application valve for the brake was nearly four feet from the nearest point on the side window. In Volume 3 of his *Great Central*, George Dow mentioned that J. G. Robinson, the CME, discussed comfort and kindred matters with his enginemen.

Was any consideration given to the difficulty of

These two ex-NBR locomotives each have cab side windows in the unusual forward position applied to that company's engines. *D. Holmes*

sighting signals past the large firebox and boiler of the later Robinson locomotive types, such as the 4-6-0s? Perhaps, once again, standardisation ruled the drawing office. In any event, in LNER days there was not enough money available to rebuild pre-Grouping engines to have left-hand drive, although there was at least one exception. This was the NER Raven 'D' Class 4-4-4Ts that were rebuilt as 4-6-2s in the 1930s on the orders of Gresley. Their power-reversing gear was removed, together with the Westinghouse air pump and brakes. Most importantly, their principal controls were moved over to the left-hand side of the footplate. It might be interesting to speculate why, in this case, the traditional right-hand drive of the NER was abandoned, particularly as these engines spent the majority of their time in the North East. Perhaps this was not intended to be an isolated change-over to left-hand drive, and that Gresley had planned a wholesale change for all LNER right-hand-drive locomotives, but in the end the accountants said 'no'.

It took until the late 1920s for the LNER to abandon right-hand drive for all new construction. For example, the later series of Gresley 'Pacifics' had the driver's controls on the left. Peter Townend, in his *East Coast Pacifics At Work*, writes that the change-over from right- to left-hand drive arose because it had been decided to standardise the new electric colour light signals on the left. After the 1923 Grouping many drivers had to adapt to both the left-hand-drive and right-hand-drive engines that had been inherited from the older companies. They had to acquire mentally two sets of signal sighting marks and 'stopping' marks at platforms.

As already mentioned, when gathering facts about controls and their positions, it became evident that the side on which the driver stood or sat rarely encouraged much comment on the part of writers. Observations on which side of the footplate the principal controls should be positioned, in relation to the positioning of the lineside signals, in both technical and lay publications, are not easy to find.

UNUSUAL CONTROLS

Among the pre-Grouping locomotives, the Lancashire & Yorkshire 'Atlantics' and 4-6-0s, for example, had the cab controls positioned so that they were in reach of the driver when he was seated. The double handle of the regulator moved horizontally within guiding brackets across the backhead so that it could be reached from either side of the cab. The L&YR also anticipated the vertically mounted reversing screw in the cab adopted by Gresley of the GNR.

A feature of the continental steam locomotive, and one rarely used in Britain, was the parallel linkage that joined the regulator spindle on the backhead to a handle close to the driver's hand. A cursory inspection of the footplate of an Austrian locomotive might not reveal the regulator because it was an insignificant-looking push-pull handle alongside the firebox.

COMPOUND CONTROLS

Ten of thousands of words have been written on the subject of compounding, and the subject has been argued over and over again. Comparative performance statistics have been used as ammunition by all parties to the argument. Fuel and water economy and the complexity of both the mechanisms and the controls have been the subject of many learned papers. From about 1880 onward a determined effort was made in France to improve the operating efficiency of locomotives. Compounding became an important contributor to performance; together with superheating and eventually feedwater heating, it enabled low coal and water consumption values to be achieved

From the 1880s onward locomotive designers in this country had to consider whether to compound or not to compound. They had to weigh the merits of fuel economy and a slight increase in complexity of the machinery against the need for more complicated controls when compared with those of a simple expansion engine. They could choose, as the French usually did, to provide two sets of independently controllable valve gear and regulators that would allow the driver to operate the engine as a simple, as a semi-compound or as full compound. If that was their choice, would it be necessary to train a select group of drivers in the correct way to handle the controls in order to make it all worthwhile? Among the railways that operated compounds, some provided independent valve gears, others did not. Some only gave the driver the option of feeding steam directly to the low-pressure cylinders when, for example, starting.

On the subject of controls that might enable a driver to operate his engine at the most efficient settings of the throttles and valve gears of a compound, we should note Brunel's opinion that things such as controls, which might distract a driver from his view ahead, should be avoided.

The first compound 4-4-0s on the Midland not only had two independently adjustable valve gear controls, but also had two regulator handles in the cab. The two-handled rotating cut-off control could be moved fore and aft so that the driver could engage it with the low-pressure valve gear or with the high-pressure or simultaneously with both. A similar combined control was developed for compound locomotives of the Nord in France.

Deeley of the Midland arranged that, for the first quarter of the regulator's movement from the shut position, steam was admitted directly to the valves of the low-pressure cylinders. Further opening of the throttle shut off the supply of steam admittedly directly to the low-pressure cylinders

and the engine then worked as a full compound. As the high- and low-pressure valve gears were not independent, there was only one cut-off/reverser control in the cab. Such a simple system would have appealed to Brunel.

O. S. Nock, when writing about locomotives, avoided making and repeating ill-judged comments. In his *Historical Steam Locomotives*, on the subject of Midland compounds, he wrote '...there is no doubt that they [the controls] called for an uncommon degree of skill and intelligence on the part of the driver,' and later on, '...the complexities of the control were thought to be too much for the average engineman.' E. S. Cox recorded the occasion when he had to instruct an experienced driver to lengthen the cut-off of a compound because at 30% or less there was insufficient steam getting to the low-pressure cylinders. Such observations might suggest, as others have, that selecting drivers by seniority rather than on ability was not a good policy.

5

THE LOCOMOTIVE CAB IN THE LAST 40 YEARS OF STEAM

A STANDARD NATIONAL BRAKE SYSTEM

When it was decided after the First World War that the majority of the railway companies would be amalgamated into four groups, the question arose 'air or vacuum brake?'. The choice was between the Westinghouse air brake, used on the LC&DR, LB&SCR, GER, NBR, NER, Caledonian, LT&SR and the GNSR, or the vacuum brake of the LNWR, GNR, Midland, GWR, L&SWR and SE&CR, to name just the larger companies. The vacuum brake was less costly to install and maintain. The Westinghouse air brake cost more but was far more effective and quicker to release. It was particularly useful when operating an intensive, short-headway suburban service, such as that in and out of Liverpool Street terminus. Rutherford in *Backtrack* (January 2000) argued that the LNER's decision, after the Grouping, to standardise on the vacuum brake rather than on the Westinghouse was a retrograde step, particularly as the number of air-brake-fitted engines outnumbered those with the vacuum brake. Conversion of rolling stock to the vacuum brake resulted in a great deal of trouble for the former NBR, GNSR and NER areas. On the one-time NER drivers compared the vacuum brake unfavourably with the Westinghouse with which they were familiar. Some knowledgeable writers have suggested that the decision to go for the vacuum brake as the national standard was the result of some behind-the-scenes dealing based on finance rather than on technology. C. J. Allen was of the opinion that at the time many of the chief engineers considered that the selection of the vacuum brake as the national standard was a mistake.

QUICK-ACTING BRAKES

Although quick-acting service valves were developed to speed up the application of the vacuum brake, and were essential for operating the LNER's high-speed trains of the 1930s, the maximum brake pressure available was that of atmosphere (14.7psi). Brake cylinders, therefore, in comparison with the compressed-air brake, had to be much larger and heavier. The brake cylinders with the Westinghouse system were smaller because the operating pressure was 70-80psi.

THE 20TH-CENTURY CAB

The following comments on individual 20th-century cabs do not include those of the Great Western for the simple reason that the railway that led the way in so many technical improvements of the steam locomotive had decided that what was good enough for 1899 was good enough for the next century. Whether or not all GWR drivers and firemen were of the same opinion is difficult to determine.

GRESLEY CABS

When Gresley's 'Pacific' No 4472 appeared in 1922 it was seen to have a cab in keeping with its size. Similarly Raven on the North Eastern had provided large side-window cabs for his engines,

Above The principal controls in the cab of a **GWR** 'Castle'. The driver's hand is on the vacuum brake lever. The cut-off/reverser pedestal and handles are not, as with earlier **GWR** locomotives, imposing a spine-bending stance. *L. A. Summers*

Below Firing the 'Castle' right-handed. *L. A. Summers*

Right Firing left-handed on the footplate of a Southern 4-6-2. *F. Rich*

The cab of an **LNER 'A4'**, with pendant regulator. The vertical cut-off/reverser pedestal and handle and the brake control and ejector are close to the seated position of the driver. The lever for the cylinder cocks is on the fireman's side. *Pendragon*

including the 'Pacifics'. By about 1930 most new-build locomotives, with the exception of those on the Great Western, had lost much of their Victorian looks.

On the East Coast route Gresley's cabs appeared to have more controls than those of other lines. They also exhibited an aura of speed and power. Both driver and fireman of the 4-6-2s and 2-6-2s were provided with padded bucket seats and with the majority of the driver's controls within his reach when seated. Completely different from the control of the larger types of locomotives of the other three members of the 'Big Four' was the vertical screw cut-off/reverser control pedestal mounted close to the driver's right knee. The vacuum brake control unit was immediately in front of the driver's right shoulder and was far more impressive than the Victorian 'shower tap' lever fitted to some LMS engines, including the 'Pacifics'. From the start all the Gresley 'Pacifics' had steam chest pressure gauges in the cab. Between 1927 and 1931 some were provided with the Ashcroft Cut-off Control Gauge, which indicated steam chest pressure and exhaust pressure to enable a driver to select the optimum cut-off.

All the 'A4s' when delivered were provided with a Flaman speed recorder, positioned on the fireman's side of the cab. The indicating face, showing an adjustable datum speed pointer and the speed pointer itself, could be seen by the driver. The paper roll on which speed and other data were marked provided valuable information about a locomotive's performance. When Edward Thompson decided to modify some of Gresley's engines he provided No 3698 of the 'A2/1' Class with a long-handled regulator in place of the pull-and-push lever. This had to be used because the usual push-pull connection to the throttle valve had been replaced by a rotating rod. This change significantly altered the interior appearance of the Gresley cab.

Using a wedge shape in plan for a cab, as on some LNER locomotives, avoided the glare from the open firedoor being reflected by the forward window glass. It also helped to keep smoke and steam away. In order to reduce the retarding effect of the induced headwind, both the front of the smokebox and the cab of many PLM engines in France were wedge-shaped in plan. The wedge-fronted smokebox and chimney went out of use as locomotives types became larger, but the wedge-fronted cab was retained and became a recognisable feature of PLM engines that survived until the end of steam.

R. H. N. Hardy commented on the controls of a Gresley 2-6-0:

'They [the 'K2' Class] were reliable but crude on the footplate and very uncomfortable for the enginemen, who had become used to GER side-windowed cabs and comfortable seating. [They] offered a small sloping plank seat, a heavy stick reversing lever and a GNR pull-out regulator up near the roof with a will of its own. All were rough riders, devoid of comfort. Young as I was I did not realise that elderly men would soon tire of wrestling with a heavy reversing lever and standing up all day in a rough, crude cab when they had been used to the armchair comfort of "D16s" [GER].'

The cab structure of Gresley's 'B17s', according to Hardy, was flimsy compared with that of the 4-6-0s they were replacing, such as those from the GER and GCR. They tended to rattle and this accentuated the rough riding characteristics. The driver and fireman had to sit in a skewed posture on the 'piano stool'-type seats because the sand boxes for the rear driving wheels took up space inside the cab. The 'B17s' used on the one-time GCR eventually had their rear sandboxes repositioned below the cab.

The provision of seats for the driver in particular was the subject of different opinions among the pre-Grouping railways. If the cab was designed so that the driver could only reach controls and look ahead by standing, then a seat was only intended for his comfort when the engine was stationary. Whereas if the controls were arranged so that the driver could remain seated, there was sometimes a conflict over space with the controls close against his knees and legs.

'THAT LOOKS ABOUT RIGHT'

When considering the history of the British footplate inevitably the question that arises is, did anyone in top management ever bother to go on to a working footplate? Or were they content to approve the arrangement of the controls on a footplate by standing at the side of the draughtsman and saying, 'That looks about right'? Instead they might have said, 'Why not move the brake control unit away from the forward window?' The reply might then have been, 'But we have always put it there.'

Powell mentions in his *Living With London Midland Locomotives* that on some Midland engines a plain regulator handle in the top quadrant meant that the driver had to stand to operate it. Even with the numerous front cab windows a driver shunting a yard had to keep moving about in order to see the shunter's hand signals. Some drivers provided their own bolt-on regulator handle extension, which enabled them to look out of the side of the cab and not have to jump up and down to move the regulator. When the LMS started to use Midland-designed engines on other parts of the system, non-Midland drivers took exception to the awkwardly shaped regulators, with the result that Derby had to extend the length of the arms. In the event of a blow-back , sending flames and steam onto the footplate, the first action to be taken was to turn on the blower. If the valve was positioned just above the firedoor, as it was on Midland engines, it would take a brave man to reach it. Of course, this may have been a logical decision based on the need to position the valve within equal reach of both crew members.

In *Royal Scots of the LMS* John Powell describes in some detail the cab of the rebuilt version. His comments include mentioning that a reversion was made to the Midland-type combined sand and blower valve in place of the Stanier-type sand control on the driver's side. Reference is also made to the 'walking stick' handles of the damper controls and to the need, sometimes, to use a piece of brick, a spanner or some string to hold them in the open position. This is a sad reflection on the thinking processes of the drawing office staff in that they could not devise a simple and effective method of holding a damper lever at a set position. The regulator was another control that would not stay where it was put. The experienced driver always carried with him a wooden wedge with which to stop the regulator handle inadvertently moving because of the vibration of the engine. Such shortcomings might have been avoided had the drawing office been mounted on a vibrating platform that would accustom the staff to conditions on the footplate. This presupposes that

Right Fashions in regulator
handles. *Author*

A Midland S&DJR 2-8-0:
   clockwise to open
B GCR: anti-clockwise to open
C Gresley 'B17: pull to open
D Southern 'Schools' Class:
   clockwise to open

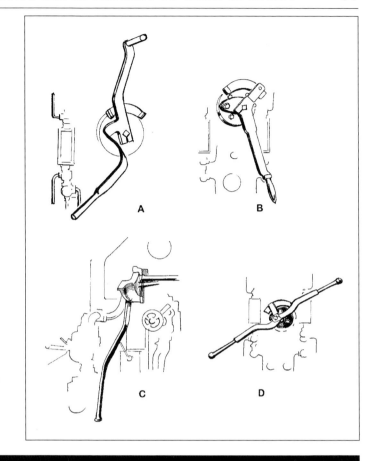

Below The regulator handle of a
Southern Railway 'King Arthur'
4-6-0, which worked in the
'traditional' anti-clockwise
direction to open. *R. H. N. Hardy*

none of them ever travelled on the footplate to see for themselves what the working conditions, particularly those of a fireman, were really like.

With the rocking-type grate, as fitted to the rebuilt 'Royal Scots' and to some other types, the fire could be disposed of quickly and easily when on shed; such a grate could also be used to 'shake up' the fire when running and dump ash into the ashpan and thus avoid the build-up of large lumps of clinker. It all looked very good on paper – it should have been the 'fireman's friend'. Unfortunately in practice such grates could jam in the open position or could not be moved at all because of a large lump of clinker getting in the way. Therefore, in general, the rocking grate was only used during fire-dropping. It was considered 'tempting fate' to operate it when hauling a train.

THE BEYER-GARRATTS

Although the 2-6-0+0-6-2 freight engines for the LMS were built by the reputable firm of Beyer Peacock, they were essentially Midland in detail. Once again the dead hand of Derby contrived to produce a very unsatisfactory engine. Among their many faults, the Garratts leaked steam from numerous joints and sometimes produced so much unwanted steam that a driver would fail the engine because he could not see the signals. The rotating bunker was intended to ease the fireman's task when on the road. However, when filling it he had to struggle with the six heavy half-doors. It usually took the combined effort of two men, and even then there many instances of fingers being trapped by the doors. Should the small steam engine that rotated the bunker fail, the fireman had to climb in and bring the coal forward to the shovelling plate.

STANIER CABS

Stanier's Class 5 'Black Fives' and 5XP (later 6P) 4-6-0s had cabs that from the side appeared to have been sat upon. The bottom line of the side sheet was lower than that of the tender, which gave the engines a 'sat down at the back' look . After the Second World War some of the 'Black Fives' were built with cabs the bottom line of which was a continuation of the running board. These, it is suggested, presented a more determined and less 'down at the back' look. Of course, such comments on aesthetics are sure to be met with derision by many readers, particularly those who wished that the graceful lines and curves of the average Victorian locomotive could have been retained until the end of steam. No doubt few enginemen in the 20th century showed much interest in the shapes and proportions of a particular engine; they had enough to contend with on the footplate without worrying about external shapes and sizes.

LMS 'PACIFICS'

When the LMS design team started laying out the cab controls of Stanier's 4-6-2s they used the precept of 'put them where we have always put them'. This meant that what had sufficed for the Class 5 would do for the new 'Pacifics'. As John Powell mentioned in *The LMS Duchesses*, the cab was not very much more imposing than that of, say, a Class 5. In some ways it was more 1900 than 1937. The regulator was a long handle extending toward the left and moving clockwise to open. Apparently the heavy long handle and vibration combined to prevent the regulator staying in one position. Therefore, as in Victorian times, a selected piece of coal or a piece of wood was wedged between the handle and the quadrant stop. The vacuum brake control lever was above and to the left of the firedoor. A rudimentary seat was provided for the driver. The overall impression was how few items of cab equipment there were for Britain's most powerful passenger locomotive. Contributing to this was the positioning of the vacuum brake ejector alongside the boiler instead of mounting it inside the cab.

If we consider the controls and their relative positions in an LMS 'Pacific' it is possible to comment on a number of details from the point of view of an ergonomist. For example, the driver's tip-up seat was hard and small – an easy comment to make, but possibly it ignores the question as to whether a driver want to sit down all the time between London and Glasgow? It also presumes that it was not practicable to bring all the controls and their attendant linkages and pipes close to the driver's hands. For the greater part of the time on a long run the driver only needed to have the regulator, the brake, sand lever, whistle and cut-off controls within reach. Once up to the scheduled speed after a stop and with the throttle fully open,

Above The **LMS 4P 2-6-4T**, with a 'limousine'-type cab in place of the earlier version that had no side windows. *Author's collection*

Right The angle plate provided on an **LMS 2-6-4T** provides some protection for the crew when operating bunker-first. *F. Rich*

Right There is no protection for the crew when running bunker-first on a **BR 2-6-4T**, even though its **Stanier** 'ancestor' has such protection. *F. Rich*

Although this photograph shows the fire of an **LMS 'Jubilee' 4-6-0** being lit, it serves to illustrate the right-hand firing stance of a fireman and how it sometimes intruded on the driver's position on the left. *Pendragon*

Right The cab of an **LMS Class 8 'Pacific'**. Note the **LMS** double sliding firedoor with operating lever, the long-handled regulator, which opened clockwise, and the vacuum brake handle close to the cut-off/reverser handles. The view forward is not obstructed by the brake ejector, as with some locomotives of other companies, because it is outside the cab, alongside the boiler. *Author's collection*

the driver might only have to make adjustments to the degree of cut-off in order to compensate for the effect of changes in the profile of the track, such as an increase in the steepness of a gradient. Provided his fireman kept the boiler pressure needle where it was supposed to be and was watching the water level, for the greater part of the time the driver concentrated on the signals and on sounds and vibrations, rather than on any instruments. In the final decade of the 'Duchesses' the AWS unit was mounted on the driver's side and within reach. At night on any locomotive the sound of the exhaust, vibrations and, sometimes, the thumping of bearings were important 'instruments'. There was no steam chest pressure gauge. The water gauge might be the only instrument given a light. In any event a partly open firedoor provided enough

illumination if any were needed. A speedometer was provided, even though it was not always considered to be essential. Of course, the majority of drivers had a built-in mental speedometer. An important help for the fireman was the steam-operated coal pusher in the tender. Keeping the back corners of the 50-square-foot grate covered meant that the fireman's forward hand on the shovel could be burned. Some fireman wore either a thick leather or a welder's glove on that hand.

BULLEID'S IDEAS

Bulleid's 'Pacifics', according to one writer, had an ergonomically designed cab even though, at the time, there was no 'Book of Good Ergonomics' available in the drawing offices at Brighton and

Above A contrast in cabs: that of the Bulleid 'Pacific' is an integral part of the 'air-smoothed' casing and provides only a limited view forward, while the cab of the BR tank engine provides a good view when working in reverse. *D. Holmes*

Left Inside the cab of a Southern Railway 'Merchant Navy' 'Pacific', with the principal controls close to the driver, together with a profusion of untidy plumbing. The AWS indicator is mounted above the vacuum brake controls in front of the driver. *Author*

Eastleigh; in any event, the word did not enter the English language until about 1950. In fact, even in his important paper of 1958, on the design of the footplate, Rich never uses the word 'ergonomics'.

Although the controls and instruments of these 'Pacifics' were grouped according to their function relative to the two crew members, there were some major failings. The vacuum brake controls obscured the driver's view forward; they were later repositioned. One of the multi-feed lubricator units was carefully mounted to ensure that, when firing, the fireman could hit his head on it. It too had to be moved. Some readers may have information on why the drawing office took such decisions in the first place. A foot-pedal was provided on the cab deck for operating the power-operated firedoors, and was positioned for use by the fireman's forward foot. However, this 'fireman's help' was eventually removed.

The inside motion and the valve gear for all three cylinders were encased in an oil bath in the manner of the sump of a car's engine. This arrangement relieved the driver of having to 'oil round' between the frames. However, it multiplied a fitter's task many times. Michael Jackman, in his

Thirty Years at Bricklayers Arms (1976), makes a cutting comment about Bulleid 'Pacifics': 'It is hard for fitters and footplatemen to understand how, after 120 years of locomotive experience, these engines came out full of snags.' The steam-power-operated reversing gear would not hold the cut-off at the selected position; the much older steam reverser of the SER engines did not drift, which prompts the question as to why it was not fitted to the Bulleid 'Pacifics'.

Bulleid's attempt, at the end of the Second World War, to design an easy-to-operate, go-anywhere and haul-anything tank engine failed. The 'Leader' Class had an 0-6-0+0-6-0, or C-C, wheel arrangement of two powered bogies under a single body that housed the boiler, the water tank and the fuel bunker as well as a driving position at both ends. The fireman was stationed amidships between the boiler and the bunker. The nautical terminology is appropriate because he had to work in the equivalent of the stokehold of a small tramp steamer. He was close-confined and very hot with a door on only one side. Among many awkward features in the stokehold was the position of the shovelling plate, set at right-angles to the firedoor.

The Ajax power-operated firedoor used on Southern 4-6-2s. Note the slots into which the manual lever could be positioned in order to provide three different fixed openings. *F. Rich*

The injector controls and rudimentary seat provided for the fireman of an **SR 'West Country'** **4-6-2.** *F. Rich*

The injector and damper controls, together with the hose for washing down the footplate, in the cab of a **'Merchant Navy' 4-6-2.** *F. Rich*

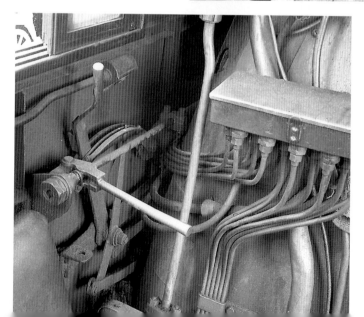

The control lever of the steam-operated cut-off and reverser system in the cab of a **'West Country'.** *F. Rich*

A door was provided to give access to the bunker so that coal could be moved forward. Should a 'Leader' be involved in a collision or derailment and it were to fall over on to the access-door side, the fireman would have been in a very dangerous situation.

The driving positions were, except for the presence of a pendant throttle lever, not unlike those of a electric multiple unit train. In that respect an attempt had been made to move away from the tradition that a driver had to share his view ahead with the bulk of the engine.

MECHANICAL STOKERS

A prominent feature in the middle of the cab of all large coal-burning locomotives in North America was the rising column of the mechanical stoker screw conveyor tube. This was controlled by the fireman from his position on the left. By selecting individual valves, he could control the different steam jets used to drive the coal off the delivery plate of the stoker, thus distributing it evenly across the grate. Mechanical stokers were tried as an experiment on a few locomotives in Britain. In France they were essential on some types of locomotive in order to keep pace, for example, with the sustained massive power output of the '240Ps' (4-8-0s) and '250Ps' (2-10-0s).

Summers and others have suggested that the provision of mechanical stokers in the last two decades of British steam, together with more attention given to improving engines in general and less to the ill-thought-out dieselisation, might have encouraged the recruitment of firemen and avoided the wasteful scrapping of perfectly good locomotives. Away from the steam railway there were often better-paid and less filthy jobs than shovelling at least a ton of coal an hour.

ADDED DANGERS

During the First World War there was virtually no interruption of train services in the UK because of enemy action. In the Second, however, there were many attacks by aircraft on trains and trains hit by bombs. The German air force did its best to destroy major industrial centres and ports, as well as the 'Baedeker' raids on historic cities such as Bath, Exeter and York.

At night drivers and firemen not only had to cope with the 'blackout' and its restricted lighting, but also had to try and keep the trains moving despite the fact that, even if they did not suffer a direct hit by bomb, a crater on the track could lie ahead unseen in the dark. In daylight there was a better chance of avoiding the effects of bombs, although in one incident a flying bomb (V1) landed and exploded only 200 yards in front of an express, giving the driver no time in which to stop.

In general, the most dangerous places to be, for obvious reasons, were within and on the approaches to large cities and ports during a major air raid. Principal stations, junctions and marshalling yards were included on the enemy's list of desirable and individual targets, together with factories and docks. The steel bulk of an engine provided some protection from bombs bursting nearby and the metal of the cab could stop a rifle-calibre machine-gun bullet. Effective or not as an air raid shelter, the crew of a steam locomotive were in a slightly better position than their colleagues who drove electric trains. Air-raid shelters were provided at large rail centres but crews tried to avoid abandoning their trains and taking shelter; if the track was intact they were determined to keep the train moving.

Modifications were made to cabs in order to prevent the glare from the open firedoor being seen by the crew of an enemy aircraft. Often this consisted of nothing more than a tarpaulin across the gap between cab and tender. Whether attempts to make a train less conspicuous were effective or not is not easy to determine. As it was, a long trail of steam, even at night, was often clearly visible from above, even if it was not illuminated by the glare from the firebox.

To some extent attacks on isolated trains was not a very profitable way of using the resources of an air force. Among the trains attacked were those that happened to be crossing a viaduct. This type of target gave the enemy the opportunity to put a route out of use for some days by destroying the structure. Otherwise, attacks on trains were mostly of the 'target of opportunity' type when an enemy fighter pilot thought he would 'have a go'. In the first quarter of 1941 alone there were 15 machine-gun attacks on trains by fighter-bombers. In November 1942 two FW 190s decided to attack a Southern train near Lydd; one of the attackers misjudged his attack and struck part of the locomotive, with the inevitable consequences.

The railways were not only financially crippled by the war, but their infrastructure had become either out of date or had been neglected. Furthermore, technical improvements, such as an AWS and colour light multiple-aspect signalling, could not be quickly extended or applied because of both a lack of money and resources. The unsatisfactory condition of much of the track meant that the speed restrictions of wartime could not be lifted. For the engine crews all this meant that the operating conditions, apart from no longer having to face bombs and bullets, were little different from those of the war years. The delight of at last seeing the railways nationalised was tempered by the fact that nothing much changed.

Therefore in 1952 much of the railway system of Britain was still that of 1945: good in a few parts but overall in need of much improvement. In some respects the Harrow disaster of 1952 can be related to the post-war operating conditions.

THE HARROW DISASTER, 1952

In October 1952 there occurred the second worst railway accident in Britain in terms of the number of persons killed and the destruction of equipment. The Harrow crash involved three trains, one of which overran adverse signals, resulting in a gigantic mountain of debris in which 112 passengers were killed and more than 300 injured. The Accident Inspecting Officer's report considered a number of possible causes. Was the driver suddenly taken ill? Had he confused the bright green signals on the adjacent electric lines for his own line? Was there a blow-back? Did steam and smoke from a freight train on the up slow line obscure the driver's view of the Distant signal? Was the driver blinded by the low early-morning sun? The official inquiry report commented on the driver's visual perceptual task in the prevailing conditions. But there was not much about the man-machine interface and some of its features that may have added to the driver's problems and started the chain of incidents that culminated in a disaster.

Analysing an accident such as Harrow raised many questions at the time. Some related to operating practices that, to the layman, seemed dangerous but were customary and within the protection of signals – provided drivers obeyed the signals correctly. The fact that a suburban train

was allowed to cross from the up slow to the up fast line so that it could precede the express engendered adverse comment in the lay press. As usual, the press devoted thousands of words to pontificating and speculating on matters that were far beyond its ken.

The primary question, out of the many, had to be that of why had the driver of the express failed to respond to the yellow light of the Distant signal, which was nearly 1,500 yards out from the Harrow Outer Home signal? Did he see the signal and not respond correctly by making a partial brake application ready to stop at the Outer Home signal if it had not been cleared in the meantime? Or had he missed the signal altogether?

This is where we need to consider more closely the control interface involved – in other words, the controls and instruments in the cab of 'Pacific' No 46242 *City of Glasgow* and, most importantly, the driver's view ahead. Against the total operating environment of the steam locomotive, the few ergonomic improvements of concern to drivers and firemen during the second half of the last century were few. In the cab of a Stanier 'Pacific' the driver's position was on the left with the principal controls arranged so that he could operate them either when seated or standing. The principal controls were the regulator, the cut-off/reverser control and the control lever of the combined vacuum-steam brake.

The front of the cab was wedged-shaped to avoid the forward windows reflecting any lights in the cab or the strong glare when the firedoor was opened. This window was the only forward view afforded the driver, apart from when he craned his neck out of the side window. The view ahead is difficult to describe accurately because there were a number of different reference eye points. There were also many different degrees of visibility and light to be considered, ranging from pitch-black through mist to intense sunlight shining into the driver's eyes. The driver might have been seated looking through the forward window or leaning out of the side window with his eyes protected to some extent by the narrow glass deflector screen mounted on the outside of the cab.

The driver's arc of vision in the horizontal plane, when seated looking forward through the front spectacle window, would have been about 20 degrees. If he was leaning out of the cab, his eye point could subtend an angle of 60 degrees. The

Inspecting Officer rode on the footplate of one of the Stanier 'Pacifics' in order to check the visibility of the up fast Distant signal. However, his report does no specify the position of his eye point or eye points. This author also checked the forward visibility factors by sitting at the controls of one of the 'Pacifics'; the forward view, either leaning out or looking through the spectacle window, was far from satisfactory. But it must be said that it was little different from that enjoyed, or rather suffered, by the drivers of Gresley or Bulleid 'Pacifics'. The accompanying illustration shows the forward view through the spectacle window of a 'Coronation' 'Pacific' approaching the signal gantry at Hatch End on which were mounted the Distant signals for the up slow and the up fast lines.

To some extent the references to the driver's eye point were academic because we cannot be certain where it was, even though the signalman at Hatch End recollected seeing the driver's face through the forward window. All that could be recorded with certainty was that the bulk of the locomotive obscured most of the forward view. Nothing unusual in that – for half a century since the arrival of the big boilers drivers had had a limited view ahead.

Among the questions considered was whether the driver misjudged how far south the train had run. There were 'landmarks' at Hatch End and a road bridge over the tracks half a mile to the north of Harrow. During the 30 to 40 seconds of his southward run toward the Distant signal, the driver may have misjudged his position and therefore was not ready to spot the yellow light during the four seconds it was within his arc of view when the visibility was reported as being 100 yards.

Was the driver distracted? As the yellow light of the Distant signal came into view through the mist and the diffused low sunlight, something might have distracted his attention from the view ahead. A sudden bursting of a gauge glass or the fracture of the bottom pipe to the left-hand water-level gauge may have filled the cab with steam and water. It needed only 4 seconds of distraction and the yellow light would have swept by unseen. After that the driver may have become unsure of how far south the train had gone. But what he most likely saw was the semaphore blade of the Harrow Outer Home signal in the 'on' position. By

The field of view through the front window of the cab of an 8P 'Coronation' Class 4-6-2 approaching the up Distant signals for Harrow. Of course, the extent of the horizontal field of view depended very much on the driver's eye-point. *Author*

then, only 600 yards ahead, was the suburban train standing at the platform. As the examination of the wrecked cab of No 46242 revealed, the brake handle was at the full application position and the regulator was closed. But by then it was too late to stop the train before it ploughed into the unsuspecting local train.

THE CHAIN OF EVENTS

A simplistic approach to determining the cause of an accident starts at the moment when someone makes a mistake, which later is seen to be the primary cause. At Harrow in 1952 the primary cause was that of the driver failing to observe and act upon the indication of the yellow light of the up fast line Distant signal. The express was late leaving Crewe and its progress south toward London was frequently affected by fog. At Watford North signal box it was brought to a stand by signals because it was closing up on a train in front. Until then the driver had been frustrated by delays. The signal eventually cleared to 'caution' and the train moved slowly through Watford Tunnel. When clear of the tunnel the signals were all 'off'. At that moment he may have relaxed to some extent because the fog was not as thick as it had been further north and the terminus was only 20 minutes away. However, he may not have attempted to run at the maximum line speed because, from experience, he may have expected further delays, particularly as he may have been mindful that his train, though classified as an express, had to defer to suburban trains making their way to the terminus and often being crossed onto the up fast line.

The signals at Hatch End were all clear, but further on the high-intensity Distant signal for Harrow was projecting a 4-degree-wide yellow beam of light. This was nearly 1,500 yards out from the up fast Outer Home signal at Harrow, which, as with the Inner Home signal, was 'on'. At the assumed speed of the Perth to London express, the yellow beam would have stayed in a driver's line of sight for only four seconds because the line curved to the left. But these conditions and times applied only if the visibility was normal. It was not. A combination of a low sun shining in the driver's eyes together with mist meant that, even if he had not been distracted, sighting the signal might have been difficult.

The object of this study of one aspect of the Harrow disaster is to emphasise that it is often necessary to look back for some way along a train of circumstances and events before assuming that a seemingly obvious cause is the real cause. At Harrow the Official Report referred to the driver's home life and whether any aspect of that and his health may have affected him to an extent that would have impaired his attention to the vital Distant signal. The Inspector decided that that was not so. The Official Report gave the primary cause of the accident as: 'I can only suggest that the [driver] must have relaxed his concentration on the signals for some unexplained reason...'. That, some might say, easy conclusion is one that has been reached on many other occasions.

ERGONOMICS AND THE STEAM LOCOMOTIVE

Our present discipline of ergonomics is not much more than 50 years old. In the 19th century and the first half of the 20th studies of the relationship between the human operator and a machine were mostly confined to work studies and to time-and-motion studies (Gilbraith in the USA). Not until 1919 in the UK was a body set up to study the working conditions of people operating machines. The National Institute for Industrial Psychology was established in the 1920s (later to become the Industrial Health Research Board). However, few, if any, of the studies were directed specifically at control interfaces, such as the steam locomotive footplate.

Consideration of ergonomics and human factors at the start of the design of a new system or machine did not really start until the 1940s. Those who founded ergonomics as a specific discipline emphasised that the human component, called 'the operator', be given equal consideration with the 'machine' component, because the former is an essential part of the exchange of information and energy. Before this desirable situation became excepted practice, any consideration of human factors had to wait until after the designer or maker of a new machine had overcome the problem of scheming a way of meeting the specification, building models, then a prototype, eliminating any snags as they occurred during the experimental stages and finally tidying up and rationalising for production. Sometimes, what we now call human factors and ergonomics just happened; sometimes they were considered, but only after settling matters that, to the designers and constructors, were far more important.

HUMAN ADAPTABILITY

Today, ergonomics enables the machine to be designed to suit the human operator. A steam locomotive, particularly the very early types, was not fitted to the driver's requirements and only the adaptability of the human frame to contorted positions enabled drivers to operate the controls and keep a good lookout. Externally, many British locomotive cabs appeared to be spacious, but closer examination would show that the firebox projected back into the cab, and springs and wheel arches took up floor space, as did some of the controls. There was sometimes room neither to sit nor stand in comfort. Often mentioned is the fact that as late as the 1950s on the former Great Western system drivers were still having to adopt a lookout stance requiring the spine to be curved.

Irrespective of the type of locomotive, its cab had to be a compromise between one that was so completely enclosed that, in summer, the crew were in a very hot environment or so open that in winter they were frozen. At the same time conditions on the footplate obviously varied from one extreme to another depending on whether the engine was stationary or moving. With some locomotives, a steam manifold supplying various ancillary systems was enclosed within the cab, thereby adding to the temperature in summer. The common practice in Britain of operating engines tender-first over long distances exposed the crew to rain and snow against which there was little protection. There are examples on record of a footplate being two or three feet deep in snow, despite the heat of the fire.

The elements in which the driver worked and that formed the footplate environment included steam and smoke, oil, grease and coal dust. There were also sounds and vibrations, variations in temperature, and the flow of air, smoke and steam over and through the cab. These factors are mentioned in order to emphasise that a steam locomotive driver was an integral part of the whole operating environment. At this point it should be mentioned that any instruments provided for use by the driver often could only be seen in daylight. At night, a driver relied very much on sounds and vibrations from which to determine speed and the well-being of his engine. Similarly, at night the fireman may have had to depend on sound to determine if an injector was working properly.

The environmental conditions obviously affected the driver's decision-making concerning how to use the potential power of his locomotive most effectively. Water, either frozen or liquid, could adversely affect adhesion and it would therefore be necessary to operate the sanding apparatus. Maintaining adhesion in order to avoid wheel slip did not necessarily only happen when starting a train; it could also occur at high speed and, if not detected immediately, might result in damage to the connecting and coupling rods.

DRIVERS' REMEDIES

Sometimes a driver had to intervene in the intentions of the designer and correct 'built-in' faults. For example, the steam-operated cut-off/reverser on London, Tilbury & Southend Railway tank engines would not stay in one position, so drivers inserted a bolt in the mechanism to keep it at about 35%. The Highland 'River' Class 4-6-0s were fitted with steam-operated reversing gear. However, this would only remain either in full forward or full backward gear, thereby, as would be said, 'breaking the fireman's back' as he attempted to meet the demand for maximum steam. The experienced drivers were known to put suitably shaped pieces of wood into the expansion links in order to effect a degree of expansive working.

The relationship between the degree of throttle opening and the cut-off selected was always a subject that engendered contrary arguments. The ideal working relationship was usually considered to be a fully open throttle and the minimum acceptable cut-off percentage, although much depended on the type of engine and type of valve gear. With some types of locomotives, power output and smooth operating were achieved with a partly closed throttle and a longer cut-off; much depended on a number of factors. However, irrespective of what the book said or the opinions of other drivers, some individuals on the footplate preferred to use their own combination of control settings. On the GNR, most drivers of Ivatt 'Atlantics', which had slide valves and a lever for adjusting the cut-off and reversing, put it into full forward gear when starting and thereafter only used the regulator to effect control. This was because the gear was so stiff to operate. This freedom of choice was, in many ways, unique to driving British steam engines. With other forms of motive power the driver has usually been constrained by precise rules concerning the use of the controls. On the footplate of a French locomotive there was just one recommended precise setting of the controls for a specific operating regime, and the *mecanicien* was expected to work closely to it.

THE 'BRITANNIAS'

Today, ergonomics enables the machine to be designed to suit the human operator. But, as mentioned, steam locomotives, particularly the

THE TYPICAL CONTROLS, INSTRUMENTS AND EQUIPMENT ON THE FOOTPLATE OF A LARGE BRITISH LOCOMOTIVE

Regulator
Combined cut-off and reversing control
   wheel or lever
Cylinder drain cocks lever
In-cab signalling equipment and
   acknowledgement lever, such as AWS
Blower valve
Sand lever
Brake controls
Injector controls
Lubricators
Boiler pressure gauge
Steam chest pressure gauge
Brake vacuum or pressure gauge
Boiler water-level gauges and shut-off cocks
Train steam heating pressure gauge
Speed indicator (sometimes provided)
Firedoor and operating mechanism
Slack pipe for watering coal
Tender brake wheel
Water scoop control wheel
Glass wind deflectors
Ashpan damper controls

This list does not include a clock, despite the fact that in most of the control positions of other forms of transport a clock was considered to be an essential item. Even as late as the 1950s not all drivers carried a pocket watch.

Until the advent of a series of standard locomotives for the nationalised railway system from 1951 onwards, the cab of the 'Georgian' locomotive in the UK was ergonomically little different from the preceding Edwardian and Victorian types.

Only in the last ten years of steam locomotive development in Britain was more thought given to the working conditions on the footplate. The BR Standard designs had cabs and controls arranged with some thought to their positions relative to the footplate crew. Drivers and firemen were invited to give their opinions on mock-ups of the cabs of the new 'Britannia' Class 'Pacifics' and other Standard locomotives. The layout of the cab had been given careful consideration in an attempt to improve their working conditions. Ergonomics, as a deliberate study, had at last entered the railway scene, even though at that time the word had only just been coined and, compared with today's situation, there was no great bank of human data and 'best ergonomics' to which designers could refer.

Despite this determined effort to obtain the opinions of drivers and firemen, the 'new' cab was not the complete success it might have been. How much the dislikes of individuals were purely subjective, biased by unfamiliarity, or were reasoned considerations of all the man-machine factors, is not on public record. The light construction of the cab made it vibrate and amplify noises. Some enginemen were put off by the unusual – to them – pendant fore-and-aft, push-pull regulator lever. Yet such a regulator had been applied to many locomotives in the UK for at least 50 years. Those enginemen from the Eastern or North Eastern Regions, accustomed to Gresley cabs, no doubt approved of it – an example of familiarity influencing judgement. Eventually some drivers found that the regulator would not stay in one position and therefore they had to contrive a method of wedging it. The cut-off/reversing wheel was edge-on to the driver and soon gained the appellation 'mangle' because it resembled the old-fashion domestic machine for wringing out clothes. An interesting detail was the cut-off indicator. This was a pointer moving over a drum mounted in the same plane as the reverser wheel. The pointer moved from full forward gear toward the zero position, then on to the reverse sector and not the other way, as might have been

very early types, were not fitted to the driver's requirements and only the adaptability of the human frame to contorted positions enabled drivers to operate the controls and keep a good lookout.

In the UK, with new designs of steam locomotive few in number during the 1940s and '50s, there was little encouragement to apply human-factor engineering to the design of the controls and their arrangement. In general, mechanical convenience still predominated.

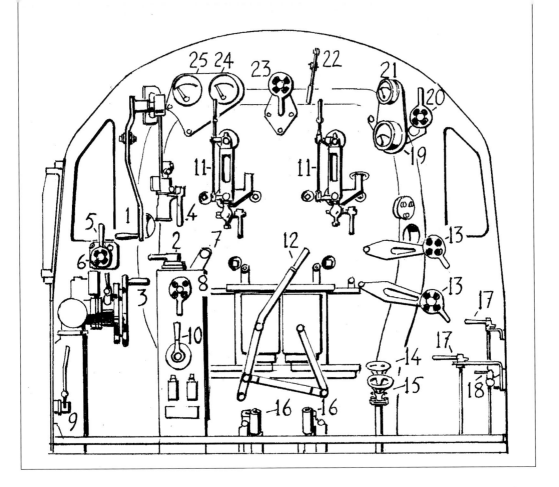

The controls and instruments in the cab of a narrow-grate BR Standard locomotive. A similar number and arrangement was also used for the 'Britannia' 4-6-2s. The AWS unit is not shown. *Author*

1 Regulator, 2 Vacuum brake valve, 3 Cut-off/reversing wheel, 4 Steam brake valve, 5 Small ejector valve, 6 Large ejector valve, 7 Release valve, 8 Blower valve, 9 Cylinder cocks lever, 10 Sanding valve, 11 Water gauge, 12 Firedoors handle, 13 Live steam injector valves, 14 Front damper control, 15 Rear damper control, 16 Rocking grate lever, 17 Injector feed water valves, 18 Tender sprinkler and coal watering valves, 19 Boiler pressure gauge, 20 Carriage heating reducing valve, 21 Carriage heating pressure gauge, 22 Whistle valve, 23 Steam manifold shut-off valve, 24 Vacuum brake gauge, 25 Steam chest pressure.

expected. Most of the 'plumbing' associated with the vacuum brake system and the driver's valve lever was hidden in a large pedestal close to his right knee; the handle moved in a horizontal plane and not in the vertical as had been the practice for more than 70 years.

The cab was considered by some to be very dirty – in other words, coal dust swirled around. Some of the firemen who were invited to comment found the shovelling plate of the tender to be set too high. A feature of the new cab was the seating position for the driver with the primary and other driver-operated controls arranged within his reach. Earlier locomotives, including Gresley's,

had included a comfortable seating position for the driver but not all the controls were within easy reach at all times and the requirements of mechanical convenience were usually dominant. Adverse comments about the footplate included concern about the driver's seat. Would it prevent a driver getting out of it in a hurry in the event of a blow-back? To some extent, the driver was protected by the large brake pedestal and the firescreen, and the blower control valve was close to his right hand and not, as with some cabs, on the middle of the backhead above the firedoor.

The application of ergonomic precepts to the positioning of the controls led to the seemingly

The driver of a 'Britannia' 'Pacific'. The pendant regulator, the cut-off/reverser wheel and the handle of the vacuum brake control are close to his seated position. *R. H. N. Hardy*

obvious arrangement of concentrating the controls used most frequently by the fireman on his side of the footplate, including the injectors. However, with both overflow pipes discharging alongside each other it was sometimes difficult at night to determine which injector was operating. Apparently 100 or more years' experience of firemen shovelling coal out of the tender and into the firebox was ignored by the designer of the tender shovelling plate or hatch; compared with 'old' tenders, that of the 'Britannia' required extra bodily movement and therefore more energy. The rotatable control handles for the front and back damper were down on the deck of the cab, requiring the fireman to stoop.

Although the obvious requirement of eliminating excessive stretching to operate the controls had been met with in the design of the 'Britannia' cab, the total operating environment had changed very little. The perceptual task was similar to that of the Victorian driver. As late as 1951, when the first of the class, *Britannia*, took the rails, there were still many signals whose indications were insufficiently differentiated from the background. Most significantly, the driver's position was still located with the bulk of the locomotive obstructing a large arc of the view ahead, particularly to the right of the track.

Only one Standard Class 8 'Pacific' was built, No 71000, but despite the experience gained from operating the 'Britannias', this enlarged version still presented the footplatemen with problems, as mentioned by Rich in *Steam World*. For example,

the lever controlling the coal-pusher required great effort on the part of the fireman, as well as being likely to crush his fingers. The reverser wheel had to be turned 30 times between full forward and full back gear because BR's 'expert opinion' decided that the Caprotti system, requiring only one turn between full forward and full back, would not be understood by the average driver. The sprinkler control valve and that for the tender spray were positioned where the fireman's legs should have been when he took the opportunity to sit down. Once again someone had been entrusted with the design of the cab who had no practical experience of driving or firing.

Despite the attempts to improve the working conditions on the footplate of the BR Standard locomotives, the design office team had failed to notice that by providing a round filling hole on the back of the tender, taking on water was made more difficult than it need have been. If, as on the continent, the filling aperture had been elongated, it would not have been necessary to position the engine so precisely. Once again it was an example of 'new wine into old bottles'; the Standard engines and their crews had to adapt to a railway that still used 19th-century equipment.

The majority of British locomotive types had a fallplate that bridged the gap between engine and tender. Should the coupling between the two part, the fireman could fall down and be killed. The 'Britannias' had a footplate that extended back as far as the front of the tender, thereby obviating the need for a fallplate. On one occasion the drawbar

Right **A BR Standard Class 2 2-6-0 with a tender cab to improve the crew's environment when operating tender-first.** *F. Hornby*

Below right **Taking on water could be a precarious operation in icy conditions.** *L. A. Summers*

between a 'Britannia' loco and tender at the head of a train failed. The vacuum pipe was ruptured, thus bringing the train automatically to a standstill. However, the engine and tender had steam-operated brakes and, with the pipe leading to the tender pulled apart, the driver could only stop by reversing the engine. Had there been the traditional fallplate, the fireman might have been killed. After that accident safety chains were fitted between engine and tender.

BRITISH AND FRENCH
FOOTPLATES COMPARED

By comparison with their equivalents in other countries, including Britain, the highly skilled enginemen in France worked in a far from comfortable environment and with controls arranged for simplicity of installation rather than for the needs of the human operators. Although the design offices schemed in all the devices, controls and instruments needed for high performance, they were often very parsimonious when it came to the size of a footplate. The fore and aft dimension was kept to a minimum with the result that the driver, or *mecanicien*, had to stand close up against the backhead and its controls. A typical dimension was 32 inches between the backhead and the gap between the front of the tender. Both the Nord 'Pacifics' and the Chapelon rebuilds, the '231Es', which worked between Paris

and the north, were good examples of short footplates. The Ouest (Etat) '231s' (4-6-2s), which took trains out of the Gare St Lazare in Paris, had footplates only two feet long. Some of the 'Pacifics' on both the Nord and the Ouest had the Pottier wind-deflecting curved screens mounted in front of the driver's unglazed forward window. These screens acted in the same way as the wind deflectors on the front of the bridge of a British warship; those readers who have seen the film *La Bête Humaine* will have noticed this arrangement. The aerodynamic screens were less effective if there was a strong crosswind, and they were only fitted to a few of the Nord and Ouest 'Pacifics'.

The firemen on the 'Pacifics' of the Ouest and of the Sud Ouest (ex-Paris Orleans and the Midi railways), as well as the famous '231Es' on the Nord regions, had to employ a firing technique that combined that of a wide and a narrow firebox. The grate was trapezoidal in plan: the back part was wide and the forward half extended down between the rear driving wheels. With this shape of grate, Chapelon's famous rebuilds of what had been some indifferent-performing 4-6-2s on the Paris Orleans, produced outstanding levels of power for their weight. Firemen on the Nord 4-6-2s had to fire a grate that was 11ft 6in long, which was also part of Chapelon's super-power '240s' (4-8-0s). However, as the outstanding performance of the first series could be limited by the endurance of the fireman, the final version, the '240P', had a mechanical stoker.

In France both the pendant pull-push and the rotating-handle-type regulators were to be found. The latter were, when compared with British practice, rather small. Throughout the history of the locomotive in France the principal control, the regulator, was always moved anti-clockwise to open. Should the reader have an interest in aircraft controls, it can be noted that up to about 1945 French throttle levers were pulled to open – that is, in the same movement as the pendant regulators.

'SPADs'

In recent years the acronym SPAD (Signals Passed At Danger) has been added to the safety vocabulary. Whenever statistics concerning incidents and accidents related to SPADs were gathered in the years of the steam locomotive, they could not include all the facts. The reported accidents and incidents from which the statistics were derived were only the tip of an iceberg. Every time a driver failed to see an 'on' Distant signal, because of poor visibility or some distraction on

the footplate, but subsequently at the last minute spotted the Home signal at danger, such an incident should theoretically have been recorded. Sometimes such failings were reported by the drivers themselves, particularly when more than one had found a signal to be badly positioned or persistently faulty. However, in general the undoubted skill and dedication to safety on the part of drivers overcame occasional errors and the difficulty of sighting a signal. Irrespective of any academic study of signal positions, shapes and colours, and variations in visibility, drivers, with very few exceptions, acquired a 'seaman's eye' when looking ahead for the next signal.

ELECTRICITY

The adage that 'electricity and water do not mix' was very applicable to the supply of electricity on a locomotive for illuminating equipment in the cab and for the headlights. Compared with the practice in other countries, there was no national UK standard – some engines had a generator and electric lights, others did not. Even simple electric lighting systems were not always favoured by shed staff; they were resistant to the environment of

An example of electrically illuminated gauges in the cab of a 'West Country' 4-6-2. *F. Rich*

steam power and the 'hard knocks' of the engine shed and in consequence were prone to fail.

'CAN YOU HEAR ME?'

In a 1930s magazine a writer used words of awe to describe a radio (wireless) link being tested that enabled the master of a hump shunting yard to communicate with the enginemen. As with all attempts to introduce electrics and electronics into a world of vibration, steam, oil and dirt, the apparatus was often unable to withstand the environment of the footplate. Thirty years on the provision of a radio link to a control centre ended the isolation of the train driver. Before such links the only contact with the operating environment was the indications provided by the lineside signals of the condition of the track ahead and of any required reductions of speed. To communicate with a control centre the train had to be stopped so that the driver or fireman could use one of the lineside telephones.

GETTING AT THE COAL

Basically the tender was a box on wheels, one part of which provided a container for the coal. From the fireman's point of view the important aspect of tender design concerned how easy it was to get at the coal. Was the bunker shaped to encourage the coal to slide forward as it was used up? Or was the bottom of the bunker level, thus requiring the fireman to go inside and move coal forward to the shovelling plate? Were the coal gates so designed that when opened the fireman was swept off his feet by a deluge of coal? The tenders of the LMS 'Pacifics' had steam-operated coal pushers and, as noted, the Beyer-Garratts had rotating bunkers in the form of a drum made to turn by a small steam engine.

With adequate coal resources the railways of Britain had little need for oil-firing. However, from time to time this alternative to coal was tried. In the case of the Great Eastern Railway it decided to make use of the oil residue from its works at Stratford. The adverse economic climate following the Second World War prompted the Government to insist that the railways equip some of their locomotives for burning oil. The policy was ill-thought-out and the scheme did not last long. Nevertheless, it introduced some firemen to a different footplate environment and to a different skill. In place of hard physical effort all they had to do was adjust a number of valves to control the flow of air to meet the demands for steam.

A typical crane-and-skip method of coaling. *D. Holmes*

Despite the drawing office's good intentions in providing a convenient stowage for the fire irons on a Southern 4-6-2, excess coal has spilled into it. F. Rich

Another aspect of the work of the fireman was the operation of the water scoop. This required prompt reaction to make sure the scoop was raised before too much water overflowed and drenched the leading coach. Injectors were often another problem for a fireman to wrestle with. They tended to be temperamental – either they refused to start or, when operating, might suddenly 'fly off'. Much depended on the type of injector fitted – some were better than others. The live-steam injectors provided by Derby were inferior to those from Swindon, but continued to be fitted after the nationalisation of the railways when such parochial and isolationist attitudes should no longer have applied.

THE RETURN OF THE COMPOUND?

Two high-pressure compound locomotives were built in Britain in the 1930s, one by the LMS, which had a semi-water-tube boiler and was a modified 'Royal Scot' 4-6-0, and the other by the LNER, which had a water-tube boiler. Photographs of their cabs disclose a most un-British array of controls. There was also Stanier's proposed compound 4-6-4, which would have incorporated all the principal 'Chapelon' features, such as, it is assumed, independent controls of the high- and low-pressure valve gears, and a valve for feeding steam directly to the low-pressure cylinders when starting. Would such complexity have been acceptable to the majority of drivers? And would they have cooperated with the need to understand fully the correct way in which the controls should be managed? Had these three compounds been built in large numbers, would there have emerged a group of enginemen trained in accordance with French practice? In that country, from about 1930 onward to the end of the steam, the performance of the locomotives, particularly in terms of power-to-weight ratios and fuel consumption, were much in advance of those in Britain and other countries. By the second half of the last century the controls and instruments on the footplate of large main-line French locomotives were a great profusion of instruments, levers and wheels.

This is where we come to the role of the *mecanicien* and his *chauffeur* (fireman). They were expected to acquire the skills needed to extract the maximum power from their machine with the minimum fuel and water consumption. Good coal in particular was expensive and scarce. Before becoming a driver an aspirant had to work for three years as a fitter, at the end of which time he could not only diagnose problems but had also acquired a thorough understanding of the thermodynamics of the steam locomotive and particularly of the way to handle a compound. Such a regime was not applied in Britain. One reason, as mentioned, was a supply of good coal so that economy of operation was less important than locomotives that did not incur heavy capital and maintenance costs.

6
BRITISH SIGNALS AND INFORMATION IN THE 20TH CENTURY

DISTANT COLOURS

In 19th-century Britain Distant signals were no different in appearance from the Home signals to which they applied: both were square-ended semaphores, usually painted red with a broad white stripe toward the end of the blade (a white spot on the Midland and South Eastern systems). From experience and, in particular, from a thorough knowledge of the route, a driver was expected to be able to distinguish one from the other. Nevertheless, there were occasions when a driver endeavouring to keep to the timetable and in poor visibility became, as it were, out of step with the progress of his train. He might have assumed that he had not got as far ahead as he had. Distraction, confusion, mechanical problems with his engine and poor visibility could, together, cause him to assume that the red light of a Home signal was that of a Distant. The Coligny Welch distinguishing illuminated 'V' alongside the spectacle lens of distant signals had come into use on some railways but, although it was a step in the right direction, the 'V' did not always stand out clearly enough.

The first step taken to distinguish a Distant signal from a Home was to cut a 'V'-shaped notch in the end of the semaphore blade. Later, a white 'V' was also painted on the blade in place of the white band or spot. When the Metropolitan District Railway was electrified 1905 it adopted a yellow light in place of red on Distant signals. The start of war in 1914 delayed further steps toward distinguishing Distants from Homes. One of the earliest substitutions of yellow for red in a Distant signal light was on the Great Central. However, the arms continued to be painted red.

At the end of the Great War the Board of Trade and the signal engineers from the principal companies jointly considered the question of the colour of the light and the arm of Distant signals. Eventually they agreed on substituting a yellow (amber) light for red as the night 'caution' indication and painting the arms yellow. The 1921 decision to merge nearly all the independent companies into four groups made it easier to implement the 'yellow for caution' light. From 1924 onward, all Distant signals exhibited a green light when 'off' and a yellow when 'on'. It is a sad reflection on the ability of those charged with ensuring the safety of train operating that it took more than 50 years to address this particular problem of the Distant signal.

FLASHING LIGHTS

With other forms of transport a flashing light was considered to be a very good attention-getter, as in lighthouses and channel buoys. Flashing-light signals were developed in Sweden where the Home signals flashed 60 times a minute and the Distant signals 50. Among the British railways that had used flashing-light signals extensively was the Furness. The LMS installed flashing repeater signals 100 yards on the approach to a few Distant signals, particularly at locations prone to a sudden formation of fog. One might have expected that a flashing-light signal would have been welcomed by all drivers, but among those who were asked to give an opinion on the subject, some said the lights were too bright and others that they should be brighter; some did not like the idea at all. At sea and in the air a flashing light was preferred, which does serve to emphasise that it is not always wise to make comparisons; the steam locomotive cab was not the bridge of a ship or the cockpit of an aircraft. It was a very special and in many ways unique place of sound, vision and movement.

As with many other developments in the 1930s, war intervened. Not only was further experiment stopped, but the flashing repeaters had to be taken out of use because they contravened the blackout regulations. Two other factors influenced decisions concerning the future of this type of repeater. One was the LMS's intention to install the Hudd 'in-cab' AWS (Automatic Warning System), which was already undergoing trials on the London, Tilbury & Southend main line. Had not the war intervened, the Hudd AWS might have been a standard system on the LMS and might have led to the quicker adoption of the BR version, and the avoidance of such accidents as Bourne End and Harrow. The second factor was the decision to replace as many semaphore Distants as possible with multi-aspect colour light signals.

THREE-POSITION SIGNALS

At a few locations in Britain three-position semaphore signals were provided, giving 'stop', 'caution' and 'proceed' indications with corresponding red, yellow and green lamp aspects at night. The upper-quadrant type by then had become virtually a standard in North America, and had the high-intensity colour light signals not been introduced, the three-position semaphore might have been used more extensively in the UK. The three-position semaphore was discussed at length during the proceedings of the Institution of Railway Signal Engineers in 1922. In general, members were in favour of it. However, a dissenting opinion thought that the 45-degree 'caution' position should not be considered to be the equivalent of the existing horizontal 'on' position of a Distant signal, which repeated the position of the arm of the Home signal to which it referred. The 45-degree position, it was averred, might lead a driver to assume that it meant 'proceed with caution' but did not necessarily indicate that the next Home signal was 'on'. To

some extent this was more a question of semantics because the three-aspect colour light signals, which at that time were coming into increasing use, could display a single yellow that meant 'caution' and not necessarily that the next signal was a red absolute stop signal. Up to the 1920s most official reports on signalling problems used the term 'danger' for the horizontal position of a Distant signal arm and not, as later, 'caution'.

A feature of British signalling was the contradiction that existed concerning the meaning of an absolute stop signal. If it was 'on', it conveyed to the driver that it could not be passed unless he received authority to do so in the form of a light or flag or, if out of sight of a signal box, verbal authority via a signal-post telephone.

At locations such as stations, where it was often necessary to bring a train forward into an occupied section, such as a platform, a subsidiary 'calling on' or 'shunt ahead' signal was provided under the absolute stop signal arm. With colour light signals a subsidiary yellow or two lunar white lights indicated that the red, absolute stop, light could be passed. Some signal engineers have argued that when a 'calling on' light was illuminated the red stop light should not be lit. This academic situation is included only to emphasise the need for route knowledge and the difficulties sometimes placed before a driver.

ROUTE KNOWLEDGE

In Britain there were numerous examples of signal gantries carrying a daunting array of semaphore signals. A typical example could be seen on the GNR main line near Finsbury Park, London, in the down direction where there were seven Distant signals side-by-side on one gantry spanning the tracks. This and similar locations with multiple arrays of signals were instances where a thorough knowledge of the location and its signals was required of every driver.

In addition to information provided by signal arms and lights, a driver's route knowledge included when and how to respond to klaxons, bells and whistles. In a typical rule book there would be numerous examples of locations at which a specific set of gong, klaxon, electric horn, bell or whistle signals indicated to the driver that his train had been moved forward far enough to clear a set of points, or could be shunted back into a

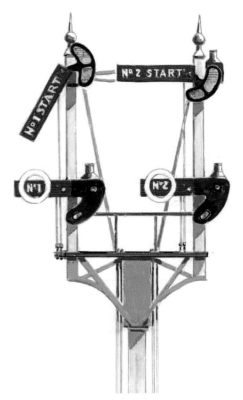

Above A common signal anomaly on some railways, particularly in the south: is the train approaching a junction signal with the high-speed route set, or do the signals refer to tracks paired by direction, with referring to the slow line and the other to the fast? This emphasises the need for route knowledge on the part of drivers. *Author*

Above GWR platform starting and shunt-ahead signals. The practice of painting on the arms the route or function that applied was acceptable in stations because a driver, even at night, had time to read the information. *Author*

Below A typical Lancashire & Yorkshire Railway signal gantry: this one at Blackpool Central has 28 signals on 14 dolls. *Pendragon*

Above **Waterloo 'A' box and gantry spanning the approach tracks: 19 signals on 15 dolls. Each arm is labelled to indicate in daylight which track it refers to. These signals lasted until 1936 when their removal significantly changed the skyline of London's South Bank.** *Pendragon*

Below left **An up East Coast express passing under the signal gantry on the approach to Durham. The signals are upper-quadrant type, in place of the former NER signals. As in NER times, the subsidiary calling-on signal has been pulled off at the same time.** *D. Holmes*

Below **NER slotted-post signals combined with a later BR-type upper-quadrant Distant signal. This presents a signalling puzzle to the layman.** *D. Holmes*

siding. Sometimes an audible signal would be used to indicate that a train could be moved out of a siding and onto the running line. An example of a gong signal was that located alongside the down line in the tunnel approaching Snow Hill station in Birmingham, which was connected to the signals and operated by a rail-mounted treadle. It provided a driver with an early indication of the signals at the exit from the smoke-filled tunnel.

The engine whistle or whistles had three purposes. One was to provide a warning of a train's approach, another was to inform the signalman of the type and destination of a train. For example, at a typical complex location drivers were required not only to announce the presence of their locomotive but to indicate in which direction they expected to be signalled. The third purpose was an essential part of working unbraked trains of wagons on which the guard, in his brake-van, had to assist in stopping a train or controlling its speed in response to the driver's whistle signals.

When comparing British and French signalling one of the first questions that arises is which of the two systems provided the clearest indication when set against a confusing background or when visibility was less than ideal. The great merit of the British Distant and Home semaphores was the fact that their shape and colours were standardised by about 1890 and could be understood by every driver on virtually every railway in the British Isles. In contrast, in France each of the one-time, pre-1938, independent companies adopted variations on the basic system of shapes and colours; however, the confusion between them and their meanings was not too much of a handicap because, unlike in the UK, there was very little need, except in an emergency such as war, for a driver to work over another company's routes. The railway companies of France kept mainly to their own sectors of the country, with Paris as it centre.

DISTRACTION

In the 19th century distraction was a factor that on a number of occasions resulted in a driver missing a signal, and it remained so in the next century. Mechanical problems continued to divert the attention of drivers, and signals came into view and swept by without being spotted. At the end of the 19th century a number of systems were

devised, tested and installed to provide a visual or aural warning to the driver of an adverse signal. Their methods of operation have been described in many publications, and they sometimes engendered the argument that they would make drivers less vigilant.

A number of accidents in the first decade of the 20th century appeared to have been caused by the inexplicable failure of a driver to respond to an adverse signal. In 1906 at Salisbury an up boat express was derailed because for some reason the driver failed to observe the speed restriction through the station. At Grantham, in the same year, an express was derailed after its driver failed to stop in the station. In both cases questions were raised about the physical and mental state of the driver. Among the many suggestions was that there should be three men on the footplate because the fireman in both accidents appeared to have failed to intervene and thereby avert a disaster. H. Rayner Wilson, one of the foremost advocates of safety devices and practices, was not in favour of such an idea. In his opinion it would involve a division of responsibility and lead to disputes. The extra man would have nothing to do and, besides being very much in the way, would enter into conversation and perhaps argument with the other two on the footplate. Furthermore, he was just as likely to be overcome by sleeplessness or drowsiness as the others. Of course, from time to time a third man would be on the footplate, perhaps an inspector or a visitor, such as a journalist.

EXPECTATION

Driving the same train along the same route day after day and never being confronted by an adverse signal led drivers to assume that signals would be clear when they were not. At Lewisham in 1957 a combination of dense fog, excessive speed in the circumstances and signals to the right of the track, together with expectation, led to a disastrous rear-end collision. The driver, sitting at the controls on the left of his steam locomotive, admitted after the accident that 'he was expecting a green'. On the Southern Region at the time there was no AWS that might have prevented the accident.

From the earliest years of the railway the operation of single lines has always had to take into account the possibility that two trains might collide head on. Various procedures and devices have been used to prevent such disasters. The most usual, in the days before the modern electronic tokenless block, was the train staff or tablet. This was a physical object on which was painted or engraved the name of the single-line section of track to which it applied. Unless a driver had the staff or tablet for the single-line section ahead, his train was not allowed to proceed. This was a seemingly foolproof system of preventing head-on collisions. Unfortunately its correct operation depended, as with so many safety systems, on a human operator. On at least one occasion the expectation that the tablet that had been handed to him applied to the section ahead led a driver to take his train onto the single line, only to collide with an oncoming one whose driver had the authority to be in the section. Expectation had led him to believe that the tablet handed to him was the correct one, but he should have looked at it and verified that it applied to the single line ahead. The starting point of this chain of errors leading to disaster was carelessness on the part of those responsible for issuing the single-line tablets, but unfortunately for the driver he had the ultimate responsibility.

SPECIFIC END DETERIORATION

Another factor that has led to disasters is 'specific end deterioration'. The circumstances are well known to many of us who drive cars, although we may not be aware of the effect. Whenever someone has driven a car, or for that matter an aircraft, for more than an hour or two and has experienced problems, such as poor visibility, heavy traffic or mechanical failures, they tend to relax as they approach their destination. This relaxation of attention has led to countless road accidents within a few miles of home. It is possible that this was the cause, or a contributory cause, of some railway accidents. The 1952 disaster at Harrow, already mentioned, is a possible example. The driver of the up express from Perth appears to have failed to see the beam of the yellow light of an electric colour light Distant signal. After a number of delays since leaving Crewe, the driver may have relaxed his attention to the road ahead because the train was within 20 minutes of its destination. But the possibility of specific end deterioration, as a contributory cause, was not

referred to directly, although it may be inferred from reading parts of the report.

SIGNAL POSITIONING

At many locations on the GWR there were junction signal gantries placed well over to one side on the right of a left-hand curve so that they could be seen as early as possible by the driver of an approaching train. Perhaps more than on any other of the railways of Britain a GWR driver had to have very good route knowledge because many signals were not in the best position relative to the track to which they applied. Some might be to the left of an adjacent track; some, as mentioned, might be over on the right with other tracks in between. There were even examples on some railways of Home signals for different routes being set one above the other alongside 'dolls' (posts) geographically arranged for diverging routes. At night the array of red, yellow and green lights would present a confusing set of information to any driver coming upon them for the first time. On the LNER and the Eastern Region, for example, drivers, signalmen and signal technicians together considered the best location for a new signal or the need to move an existing one because drivers were having trouble in spotting it against its background or in minimum visibility.

NORTON FITZWARREN

Confusion can be the starting point for a chain of events that leads to disaster. At Norton Fitzwarren in 1940 the driver of an express, a very experienced and competent man, failed to react correctly to the warning siren of the GWR Automatic Warning System because he assumed he was on the main line and not on the adjacent relief line. He was reading the signals applying to the main line, which were 'off' for a train on that line, as applying to his line. At the last minute, as the train on the other line overtook his, he realised that he was not on the line he thought he was. It was too late. The trap points at the end of the relief line derailed his train. Contributing to the driver's confusion was the positioning of the signals for both lines. Some were to the left of the relief line and to the right of the main line. To the west of Taunton West Junction the relief line Home signal and the main line Home signal were side by side and on the left of both lines. Those responsible for the positioning of the signals, relative to the tracks to which they applied, may have assumed that no driver would ever be confused.

The official report on the accident recommended that signals be sited so that drivers could verify on which track they are travelling; they should not be placed just where there happened to be room. Another factor that may have been considered was that of the well-known 'expectation' trap. During the time the train was waiting at the relief line platform at Taunton the signalman may have pulled off the relief to main line signals. These could have been noticed by the driver and therefore he was expecting his train to move across onto the main line. However, subsequently the signalman may have changed his mind about holding the newspaper train that was approaching on the main line and therefore replaced the relief to main signals without the driver of the passenger train noticing the change. In addition to the initial confusion over which track he was on, the driver's attention may have been impaired by ill health and concern at his house having been destroyed during an air raid.

SPEED SIGNALLING

In France and North America in particular, 'speed signalling' was the norm, whereby a driver was given an indication to show the maximum safe speed for the route ahead – he was not necessarily given, as in Britain, an indication of which route had been set.

The LMS endeavoured in the 1930s to replace most of the main-line semaphore Distant signals with high-intensity colour lights. The advent of electric colour light signals improved both day and night sighting, and eventually their flexibility of application allowed the provision of additional indications, such as a 'double yellow', which usually meant that the next signal was a single yellow. On the LMS it could also mean a reduction of speed for a diverging route. At Bourne End in 1945 the driver of an up express came upon a double yellow followed by a clear Outer Home signal, not a single yellow. The next signals were splitting Homes indicating that the crossover ahead was set from the fast to the slow lines, with a speed limit of 20mph. It was estimated that the train was travelling at 50mph when it reached the crossover set to the slow line. The train was wrecked. The driver appears to have forgotten the special notice warning drivers that all trains on the up fast were being put across to the slow at Bourne End. He did not respond to the double yellow and reduce speed. Even if he had, the double yellow meant two different things depending on where it was located.

Whether or not drivers were consulted on the subject, the signal engineers of the different railways in the UK debated at great length in the 1920s the merits of 'speed signalling' as opposed to 'geographical' signalling (where a signal was provided for each diverging route ahead). The LMS installed an isolated stretch of colour light 'speed' signalling between Heaton Lodge Junction and Thornhill Junction, West Yorkshire; on this stretch of line a driver was confronted before a junction by one of eight different combinations of red, yellow and green lights.

A form of 'speed' signalling was also used in some 'hump' sorting yards. The hump master indicated to the driver of the engine pushing the wagons up the incline of the hump whether he should stop, proceed to hump slowly or hump at normal speed. Position light signals located alongside the track displayed three white lights set horizontally for 'stop', three at 45 degrees for 'hump slowly' and three vertically for 'normal speed'.

One difference between manually operated semaphore signals and multi-aspect colour light signals was the additional information that could be conveyed by the former to a driver by a signalman. Sometimes a form of speed signalling was used whereby, at the approach to a diverging route requiring a reduction of speed, the Home signal would be kept 'on' by the signalman until a train's speed had been reduced sufficiently. Also, a signalman might deliberately delay clearing a semaphore signal as an indication to the driver to slow up in order to avoid having to stop further on because a preceding train was taking longer than usual to clear the block. With a colour light signal its aspect could only change instantly as the appropriate button, lever or track circuit was operated; the signal could therefore not be operated as described above to give additional information.

Another type of signal was the speed warning

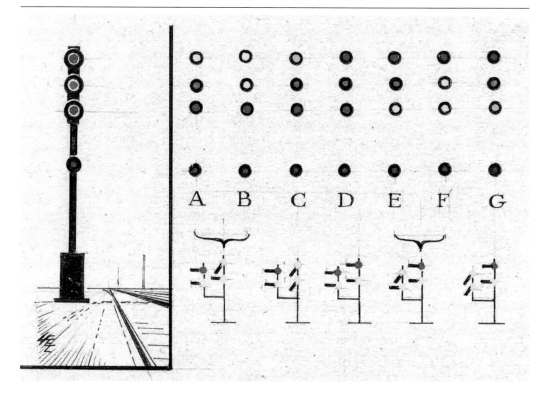

One of the few examples of speed signalling in the UK, between Heaton Lodge Junction and Thornhill Junction, with the equivalent 'geographical' junction signals below. Even had this system proved acceptable for all locations it is doubtful that its installation throughout the country could have been afforded. *Author*

High-speed route
A Caution
B Pass next signal at reduced speed
C High-speed route clear
D Stop

Low-speed route
E Caution
F Pass next signal at reduced speed
G Low-speed route clear

board. This indicated that a temporary speed restriction started at that point and remained in force until an 'end of restriction' board came in sight. Great reliance was placed on drivers when they signed on to read the notice boards indicating where they would encounter temporary speed restrictions. These boards with their oil lamps were sometimes vandalised or stolen, and their oil lamps sometimes gave a very feeble light.

ADVANCED WARNING

Until the advent of AWS in the UK, little attempt was made after the 1923 Grouping – except for the ATC of the GWR and the Hudd system on the LMS – to provide drivers with some form of indication that advised them they were passing an

adverse Distant signal. Admittedly, the illuminated 'banner' type of Distant signal repeater was sometimes provided at locations where the approach to a signal was obscured by lineside structures. Apart from the isolated LMS experimental flashing signals, no such warning was provided at all Distant signals as a standard to allow for dense fog conditions. Did cost outweigh safety?

When plans were being prepared in the 1920s for a Channel Tunnel railway, an interesting proposal was tabled for the signalling system. To provide advanced indication of the setting of a signal, a row of electric lights would extend for 100 yards between the rails on the approach to the signal, exhibiting the appropriate colour – green, yellow or red. The system was intended to keep trains moving after leaving the tunnel and running into dense fog. Such a method of providing drivers with an early indication of the aspect of the next signal may not have been practicable for the existing railways because of cost, maintenance and the exposure to damage.

STEAM AND SMOKE

As well as having to share the view ahead with precipitation and an ink-black night, a driver might have to contend with the steam and smoke emitted by his charge and from other locomotives in the vicinity. In industrial districts, atmospheric pollution, in the years before the Clean Air Act of 1956, could further add to the signal-sighting problem. There are many examples in the records of drivers complaining that they could not see ahead because of steam and smoke beating down alongside the boiler. David Jones on the Highland Railway devised a chimney with louvres that led air up into an annular surround to the inner part. This was intended to provide an upward rush of air and so prevent the exhaust from beating down. However, it was not copied by other Chief Mechanical Engineers who, it might be presumed, were not convinced that it was effective.

An interesting 'aerodynamic' feature on the forward rim of the chimney of some locomotives was the 'capuchon'. Some of the LNWR 'Alfred the Great' Class 4-4-0s had capuchons, others did not; all the 'Benbows' had them, as well as the tank engines of the LT&SR, which had large examples. Taken to the extreme, why not do away with the capuchon and simply make the chimney taller? Opinions among those who thought about such matters were divided. Did some drivers find that the capuchon kept smoke and steam away whereas others could see no reason for it? How could a raised segment of the circumference of the chimney top help to lift smoke and steam? Perhaps it was a 'fashion' item, giving an engine a certain 'look'. An incidental comment has to be why was the raised portion of the rim of the chimney called a 'capuchon', which means a 'hood' (OED)? The French used the term *visière* ('visor') for the raised rim, and *capuchon* for a movable lid to cover the chimney when an engine was out of use.

In the last century the problem of smoke and steam obscuring the driver's forward view became more severe when locomotives were given large-diameter boilers – particularly in an oncoming wind striking at an angle to the centre-line of an engine. As an experiment, a Gresley 'Pacific' had the front of its smokebox disfigured by an air duct that led upward and around the chimney; a similar idea had been tried on a GNR 'Atlantic'. These and many other arrangements of slots and plates were tried, but none was very effective. It took some years before it was realised that the solution was not the creation of an up-draught at the chimney. Wind tunnel tests demonstrated that smoke was being sucked into the vacuum created at the side of the boiler. The German type of

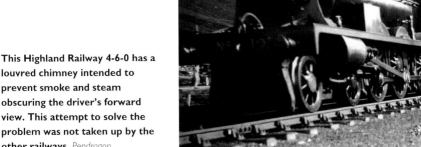

This Highland Railway 4-6-0 has a louvred chimney intended to prevent smoke and steam obscuring the driver's forward view. This attempt to solve the problem was not taken up by the other railways. *Pendragon*

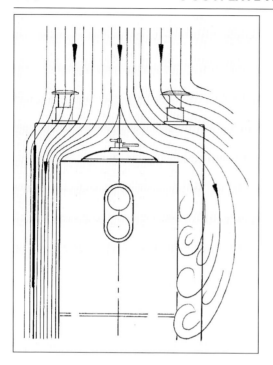

Airflow patterns with and without a deflector for preventing steam and smoke clinging to the side of the boiler. The problem was particularly acute in a crosswind. *Author*

A 'West Country' 'Pacific' demonstrating its ability to obscure completely the driver's forward view. In this example the 'air-smoothed' aerodynamically designed casing has failed to do its job. *R. H. N. Hardy*

smoke deflector plates provided the solution. The bluff front of the original 'Royal Scot' Class deflected air in the form of a bow wave. Interestingly the GWR express 4-6-0s did not suffer from smoke obscuring the view ahead, and neither did their progeny, the LMS Stanier 5XP (6P) 4-6-0s. Yet in the end the more massive boiler of the LMS rebuilt versions had to be given deflector plates.

When the double-chimney Kylchap arrangement was fitted to Gresley 'A3s' the 'soft' exhaust, when running at short cut-offs, was sucked down into the vacuum at the side of the boiler. By adding German-type deflector plates the problem was solved and, incidentally, the class acquired a more thrust-forward look. Of course, smoke deflectors were sometimes positioned directly in the driver's forward line of sight and therefore could obscure a driver's view of signals, as happened at Milton in 1955. The records suggest that in the case of a proposal by Doncaster to build a streamlined version of the 'A1', with a

front similar in shape to that of the 'A4', it seems that the REC was not officially aware of the problem from smoke obscuring the forward view and, even if it did know about it, would not have authorise the additional cost of a Bugatti/Gresley-shaped front..

An example of a system that, when adopted by British Railways, had unforeseen consequences, particularly for the footplate crew, was the Franco-Crosti 'economiser' arrangement of boiler and feedwater heater. When applied to some of the BR 9F 2-10-0s, smoke and steam from the chimney, which was at the side of the boiler and close to the cab, often obscured the forward view from the footplate. In Italy, where there were many locomotives with the Franco-Crosti system, the chimneys were taller and the problem did not arise. When, in an attempt to prevent the exhaust beating down on the cab, the blast was sharpened, the resulting increased back pressure negated the fuel-saving benefit of the system.

Incidentally, the plates at the side of a

smokebox are usually referred to as 'smoke deflectors' when, pedantically, they should be called 'air deflectors', because that is their purpose.

MILTON

When the 'Britannia' 4-6-2s began operating between London and Cardiff their drivers had to adapt to sitting on the left and not standing on the right of the footplate, as they had always done on GWR locomotives. In November 1955 at Milton, the driver of a 'Britannia' failed to observe that the Distant signal was 'on' or to respond to the siren of the GWR ATC system; further on, the bracketed Home signals indicated that the 10mph turnout was set to take the train off the up main and on to the up goods line. The train was derailed, having taken the turnout at about 50mph, and it was subsequently discovered that the ATC may not have been functioning correctly. Even though it may not have provided a full automatic brake application, the driver was still responsible for observing the lineside signals. This is where history added to the driver's visual task because, as already mentioned, on the one-time GWR lines many signals were positioned on the right of the track, providing an earlier sighting for a driver standing on the right-hand side of the footplate. Approaching the Milton turnout from up main to goods, both the Distant signal and Home signals were on the right of the main line. An additional obstruction to the driver's forward view were the handrails on the smoke deflectors, which were subsequently removed.

A faulty cab signalling system failed at Ludlow on 6 September 1957 when a driver ran through the Distant, Home and intermediate stop signal resulting in a rear-end collision with the preceding train. The siren of the GWR ATC equipment was blocked by cotton waste.

With most incidents and accidents there is a chain of events and circumstances; they may seem to be unrelated but, when taken together, provide a possible cause. For example, with accidents similar to that at Milton, did the crew pay sufficient attention to notices that included a warning that all trains would be diverted from the fast line to the slow or goods loop at certain points? Was there a good and essential working relationship between driver and fireman? Was the driver unfamiliar with the locomotive or the signals? Was his home life stressful? Was the design of the cab and its equipment adequate?

Another question, and one that has often been raised at an accident inquiry, concerned the role of the fireman and if and when he should have watched out for signals. The answer or answers to such a question depended very much on the working conditions, which varied among locomotive types, types of train and their speed, and the design and equipment of the footplate, together with many other factors.

F. Rich presented a work-study based on the locomotive of a semi-fast train on a winter's evening, using two different footplates as examples. One, the ideal, was well-equipped and arranged, the other had faulty components. He submitted that on the ideal footplate a fireman was able to devote about 40% of his time to looking out for signals, provided, that is, there were no unexpected events. On the less than ideal footplate, there was theoretically virtually no time remaining for looking for signals. In any study of the work of the fireman it is interesting to note that BR set 1.5 tons of coal per hour as the physical shovelling limit of the average fireman.

With respect to the last criterion and the official verdict that the Milton accident was primarily the driver's fault, the words of Professor Alan Earnshaw in *Steam World* are apposite to the majority of accidents that involve human actions or inaction.

'None of these innovations [track circuits, multiple-aspect colour light signals and block signalling controls] obviated the need for awareness and vigilance by railway staff of all grades. There is no escaping that fact and it has always been the official view. But were all accidents simply to be ascribed to human error and the failings of railwaymen in their daily operations? Based on an extensive study of the subject, I think not! Much greater responsibility lays at the hands of railway management, who should have ensured that conditions in which men were working were such as to reduce the elements of error caused by poor conditions, over-work, tiredness, inadequate equipment, resources and so on.'

Electrification, particularly the 25,000-volt contact wire of the catenary only a few feet above, introduced a new set of hazards for the enginemen. No longer could the long fire irons be waved above the loading gauge or the fireman be allowed to climb on top of the coal. Likewise, at all times, when stepping down from the footplate, the enginemen had to keep in mind the unprotected lethal third rail of the Southern lines.

IN-CAB SIGNALS OF THE 20TH CENTURY

The annual number of collisions, particularly the rear-end type, which had been an unfortunate feature of Victorian railways, continued in the 20th century at about the same yearly average. After each one came the inevitable question: why not repeat the indication of each signal by means of some sort of apparatus in the locomotive cab? As mentioned, from the very early years inventors had experimented with systems intended to supplant or work in concert with lineside signals. By the end of the first two decades of the 20th century in the United Kingdom there were at least five automatic warning systems either in use or being evaluated:

- the Automatic Train Control (ATC) of the GWR, which in 1912 was being installed on its main lines
- the Reliostop and Brown-Mackenzie systems of the Great Central
- the 'trip-cock' equipment on the electric trains of the Metropolitan District
- Raven's train-stop and cab signalling system on the North Eastern
- the Sykes SYX electro-mechanical equipment being evaluated on the GER, and
- the Drummond system tried on the L&SWR in 1911.

Of these only the GWR and Metropolitan District systems were used extensively. The GCR, NER and Metropolitan adopted a comparatively simple system whereby when a signal was displaying a red light a co-acting metal arm beside the track was raised. If a driver failed to react to the signal, the arm came in contact with the lever of a trip-cock in the train's brake pipe and opened it, thereby applying the brakes. The GCR system was installed, starting in 1916, along 40 route miles. Despite good

intentions among some on the railways, none of these systems survived for long after the Grouping.

Raven's cab signalling equipment, used on the NER main line, also initiated an automatic brake application in the event that an adverse signal was passed. Although this system was a notable step toward greater safety it was not, in modern terminology, failsafe. No sound on the in-cab whistle did not necessarily mean that the system was working correctly. In a further development it operated a display of miniature semaphore arms on a cab-mounted instrument in front of the driver.

Of the above systems, that of the GWR is another example of that company's success in many areas of railway technology. In the 1900s it started developing its own 'in house' method of conveying to the driver the indication of the signals by means of a warning siren if the signal being approached was 'on', or a bell if it was 'off'. As with the very successful Lartigue system of 1874 in France, a ramp between the rails on the approach to a signal was energised electrically if the signal was 'off'. When passing over the ramp, a pick-up shoe under the locomotive energised a solenoid that in turn sounded a bell and held a valve in the brake pipe closed. If the signal was 'on', the ramp was not energised and when the shoe was raised as it passed over the ramp it opened a valve in the brake pipe, thereby applying the brakes and sounding a siren. There was no visual indicator as such in the cab. The driver was provided with the means to override the automatic application of the brakes. This factor, as with all such systems, led to the question as to what extent, if at all, should the driver be allowed to intervene in the automatic action of a system? Should the driver be able to intervene and override the automatic action? Should it only warn, by means of visual or audible signal means, that a signal about to be passed was 'on'? Would the driver be affronted by the implication that he was liable on occasions to miss a signal? Furthermore, any system had to fail safe – in other words, be unable to give a false indication. If it failed to meet this fundamental requirement then it would not be trusted by the drivers. History was to prove that such questions on the GWR were answered to the satisfaction of drivers, signalmen and management. An important feature, not present in some other systems, was the provision of two positive indications, the warning siren and the 'signal off' bell. The GWR ATC become an important contributor to safety and to keeping trains on time during fog. There were far fewer incidences of danger signals being inadvertently missed on the GWR than on the other railways of the United Kingdom.

As already mentioned, on its LT&SR section the LMS installed the Hudd inductive, non-mechanical system of automatic warning. Had the Second World War not intervened it is possible that the Hudd system would have been extended over all the main lines of the LMS. Eventually, following a number of SPAD (signals passed at danger) accidents, such as Harrow, in the 1940s and '50s British Railways adopted an improved version of the Hudd as a national standard. This was the Advanced or Automatic Warning System (AWS).

The official report into the 1952 Harrow disaster referred to the lack of any form of automatic warning system or, as it was erroneously called, automatic train control. The report dealt at length with the development and application of such systems to the railways of this country. It referred to the trials of the Hudd system on the London, Tilbury & Southend lines and to the work of the Railway Executive directed towards combining the best features of the well-tried and extensively used GWR contact system with the non-contact or inductive type, such as the Hudd. The report acknowledged, and in doing so indirectly answered much ill-informed criticism of the London Midland Region, that just to install warning control would only solve a part of the problem of preventing accidents. All operating systems and equipment had to be brought up-to-date equally. For once the lay press was on the right track, even if it still tended to get hold of the wrong end of too many sticks in questioning the absence of warning control that might have prevented the Harrow disaster. But the press and other critics were wrong when they implied negligence on the part of the railway because, as the report emphasised, full-scale trial installations had been carried out in August of that year. The design was settled on a warning system to be fitted to all locomotives that would alert a driver to a restrictive signal aspect and require him to acknowledge the indication. Furthermore, should the driver fail to take any action, the brakes would be applied automatically.

AWS became standard over much of British Railways. Harrow highlighted the subject of automatic warning systems but was not the reason for its adoption. As noted, that had been decided well before the accident, and had the difficult post-war events, with their restrictions on capital expenditure, not intervened it is likely that faster progress on the more extensive adoption of this important link in safety would have been achieved. As it was, British Railways was still able to plan for nearly 2,000 route miles of AWS-equipped track and for 10,000 sets of locomotive and train equipment to be installed in just over 10 years after Harrow.

Any system that gave the driver an indication in the cab of the aspect of a signal was an important contributor to safety. It was difficult to argue against it on technical and operating grounds. However, as with so many proposed safety devices, non-operating and non-technical people had to have their say. Accountants, with one eye on the shareholders, tended to baulk at the capital cost of installing in-cab signalling throughout a company's network. Sometimes there were objections raised by the operating side on the basis that any special equipment, particularly if it was electrical, added to the cost of maintaining the locomotives. There was also a debate on the comparative merits and costs of in-cab signalling and high-intensity colour light signals. But, as noted, at Lewisham high-intensity colour light signals did not prevent the accident, whereas AWS might have.

In the mid-1930s both the LMS and the LNER introduced what were, for the time, 'high-speed trains'. Both the 'Coronation Scot' of the former company and the 'Silver Jubilee' and 'Coronation' of the latter operated schedules requiring sustained speeds well above the average. Except for some stretches of multi-aspect colour light signalling, the drivers of the two LNER trains worked in an operating environment, in terms of the view ahead and its signals, little different from that of the 19th century. 'Double block working' was applied so that a clear Home signal indicated that the line was clear for at least the next two blocks. This provision related very much to the limited braking power available. As for any potential hazards, such as a sudden obstruction occurring within the braking distance of the train, except for the greater mass and therefore energy of the train a driver was in no different a situation from that of earlier times.

7
FOOTPLATE AND SIGNALS IN WORDS AND IMAGES
...OR NEVER LET THE FACTS SPOIL A GOOD STORY!

The power and speed of the steam locomotive, in comparison with other forms of locomotion, were reflected in the writings of their time. The status of drivers was high in people's imagination, and many aspired to take their place on the footplate.

RAILWAY BOOKS

The demand for railway books never seems to wane. The seeker after railway histories in this century and in the last has been well served by both books and magazines. Even though by 1845 there were more than 15 journals whose title included 'Railway', they did not provide much information for the laymen seeking to learn more about the inner workings of the industry. *The Railway Times* first appeared in 1837 and *The Railway Magazine* in 1897; the latter would become for many years the principal source of information for the laymen.

In the 19th century 'railway' books intended for general readership, and which described how a railway and its trains worked, were thin on the ground. Furthermore there were not even many books for the professional engineers and for those who managed and controlled the railways, more particularly for those who drove and fired. Out of a list of 400 technical books in a catalogue of the late 1870s, only about a dozen covered railway subjects. Scarcely any were concerned with the work of drivers and firemen, nor was much attention given to signals.

In the Edwardian era books for those fascinated by the technology of the railways began to appear

more frequently. By the second half of the last century enthusiasts were presented with a wealth of titles, but again not many discussed the locomotive cab or signals and the work of the enginemen. It is impractical, because of space limitations and the risk of sending the reader to sleep, to list every 'locomotive and signal' author and their works. Therefore this review has to be limited to the 'stars' of the railway book and magazine list. Perforce, the list is limited to British authors, with one exception, to be mentioned later.

Dickens is the epitome of mid-Victorian popular writers. He set many of his well-drawn characters against the 'seething' lower orders and the 'great unwashed' of the times. Yet, in doing so, he only occasionally mentioned the railways, even though by mid-century the steam, smoke and noise of trains were increasingly becoming a part of people's lives. However, he does let one of his characters commit suicide by stepping off a platform into the path of an oncoming train – although he does not comment on the shock such a terrible tragedy must have had on the driver. One of his tales of the supernatural is 'No 1 Branch Line: The Signalman' from a collection entitled *Mugby Junction* – but if a reader at the time expected to find out about the specialised tasks and equipment of signalmen he would have been disappointed. However, in another story he did mention the semaphore signals whose arms were 'shaving the sky'. In *Our Mutual Friend* we can read:

The railway, at this point, knowingly shutting a green eye and opening a red one, they [the travellers] had to run for it ... all

'Monsters breathing fire and smoke.' *Author*

knowingly shutting up their green eyes and opening their red ones when they prepared to let the boofer [sic] lady pass.'

Those who have analysed the chronology of the book have suggested that Dickens did not understand the meaning of the 'red and green eyes'. The scene he describes was set at a GWR station in the 1850s, when the railway had not completely abandoned the time interval system of preventing rear-end collisions.

The searcher after details of railway operation will be disappointed with *Mugby Junction* and *Calais Night Mail* (1866). The former includes a humorous description of the staff and food in a refreshment room, while the latter is mostly set on board the Dover-Calais steam packet. In his description of the train journey down to Dover, Dickens does evoke the sensation of a train rushing through the stations and the bucolic countryside:

'Bang we have let another station off and fly away regardless. Everything is flying. The hop gardens turn gracefully towards me, presenting regular avenues of hops in rapid flight.'

However, such visual impressions were not for the driver, for he had to keep his eye on the road ahead.

Despite using the railway to provide a dramatic and colourful background to some of his characters, Dickens rarely wrote about the enginemen. One of the few examples is an engineman in *Dombey and Son* (1848). Mr Toodles was a stoker on the London & Birmingham Railway. Presumably Dickens decided that a name such as Toodles evoked the image of a fireman.

'He was dressed in a canvas suit abundantly besmeared with coal-dust and oil, and had cinders in his whiskers, and a smell of half-slaked ashes all over him.'

The smell of slaked ashes is evoked but not, for some reason, the unforgettable combination of the aromas of coal or coke smoke, hot steam and metal and hot oil and grease that most of us associate with steam power.

It is difficult to determine to what extent Victorian boys were 'ferroviaphiles'. In Routledge's *Every Boy's Annual* for 1873, for example, none of the stories concerned the railway. The few articles dealing with technology concentrated on weapons.

Up to about 1890 there were only about a dozen writers who might be described as being 'railway' authors. Among the few was Michael Reynolds. His railway career included being a driver on the

A typical Victorian representation of the footplate. *Author*

LNWR and a Running Shed Superintendent on the LB&SCR. Therefore he wrote from practical experience. He is best known for his *Engine-Driving Life* (1881) and *Locomotive Engine Driving* (1877). Admittedly, the latter was aimed at drivers and not the interested public. The technical magazine *The Engineer*, in its review of the book, commented, 'He has supplied a want and he has supplied it well,' a judgement that emphasised the lack of books both for railwaymen and, in turn, for the interested laymen.

The Daily Telegraph (16 November 1877) related Reynolds's *Locomotive Engine Driving* to the 'railway' words of Dickens, although it refers to Toodles as the engine driver, not the stoker.

'Charles Dickens has drawn attention to some few of the many virtues of engine-drivers in his inimitable sketch of Mr Toodles, the father of the dissolute Rob the Grinder. Dickens, however, had not sufficient acquaintance with the practical working of a railway, and the dangers and difficulties to which an engine-driver [sic] is almost hourly exposed, to do more than suggest the good qualities that in Mr Toodles shine conspicuously through his oily and dusty apparel, and betray themselves under a huskiness of voice which he attributes to

constant irritation from the ashes. A little volume by Michael Reynolds will give the general reader, if he will take the time to grapple with the technical details of a practical manual for the use of the working locomotive-drivers, some slight notion of what their dangers and difficulties really are.'

One passage from Reynolds's *Engine-Driving Life* provides a useful summary of the driver's work and at the same time his pride in his calling:

'The fiery courser has all the marks of "go" about her, and young hearts and young life can already hear her pounding through space and roaring over the rails. At the appointed hour she is in steam, and stands foaming upon the iron track, impatient to be hitched on to the special. As soon as Her Majesty has arrived at the station, a very few minutes intervene before she gives the order to start. A few clear, sonorous puffs, and the huge creature begins to stretch its sinews of brass and muscles of iron, saluting the weary cars in the sidings as it begins to feel the pressure of the load. When a driver has combined his knowledge of the signals and their position with his knowledge of the road and its gradients, he can then run with confidence, without the least fear of losing control over the train.'

Undoubtedly, the foregoing is a much romanticised view of a driver's work that ignores the reality of an environment that combined in varying proportions and at varying intervals extremes of heat and cold, driving rain, sleet and snow, together with vibration. Such realities of life on the footplate were rarely mentioned by writers.

Apart from the inhabitants of very remote hamlets, the majority of people in Britain in the last quarter of Victoria's reign were within walking distance of the railway. By then the railways had become an integral and essential element of society and commerce. However, the principal writers of fiction in those years rarely set their characters against a railway background. Even Conan Doyle rationed his references to rail travel. Few of the adventures of Sherlock Holmes involved investigating track and train events. Rarely do Holmes and Watson stroll down the platform and admire and comment upon the engine, in particular its cab and controls, at the head of their train. Of course, in most of the stories involving travel by train they were in a hurry and did not have time for such, to them, immaterial interests. However, in *The Bruce Partington Plans* Conan Doyle became involved in technicalities. The story concerned a body thrown onto the roof of a passing Inner Circle train on London's Metropolitan Railway. Subsequently it rolled off to the side of the track because of the lurching of the train passing over the junction at Aldgate.

In another story Holmes is credited with the ability to determine the speed of a train by counting the telegraph poles per minute as they passed, but neither he nor his chronicler Watson comment on the type of locomotive at the head of their train. Even though Conan Doyle interested himself in scientific and technical matters, to the extent of building an electrically powered monorail in his garden, he must have decided that his readers would not be interested in too much railway technology. However, in one of his non-Holmesian tales, *The Vanishing Train*, he goes into operating technicalities in some detail but, unfortunately, constructs a plot that is far removed from the real world of the railway and which involves inserting a turnout to a siding in between the passage of two trains. The driver and 'stoker',

as so often happens in railway fiction, have a fight on the footplate.

Reading *The Boy's Own Paper Annual* for 1896/97 highlights again how few of the contributors wrote about railways. Checking the index under 'R' produces no railway subjects, and none under 'S' for steam or 'T' for train. 'L' provides Locomotive Engine Cleaning. This article was intended to encourage readers not to be put off such a career by the strenuous and dangerous nature of the job. The concluding paragraph reads:

'I wish all cleaners and would-be cleaners, who may read this, every success in their arduous labour, and conclude with the hope that some future driver of the Queen may take heart from my words and persevere to the end.'

The obvious question is: were the ambitions of the middle- and upper-class readers of the *BOP* aimed at such an occupation?

The tendency to eschew technical details in both Victorian and Edwardian writing may have been a reflection on the then sharp social demarcation that existed between the oily handed sons of toil and the better-educated and cleaner middle and upper classes. The technical details of the world of the tradesman and the mechanic, and in particular of the engine drive and fireman, as with the artist and the actor, were not considered to be matters in which a gentleman should become interested.

At the end of the 19th century there was an increasing attention to the competing services offered by the different companies from London to Scotland by the West Coast, by the Midland Railway, or by the East Coast route: the so-called 'Railway Races to the North' from London Euston and London King's Cross to Aberdeen made the headlines. Performance, as expressed in speeds and train loads, was given fairly good coverage in the technical journals such as *The Engineer*. *The Railway and Travel Monthly* was notable for its series on express trains and locomotives, containing a wealth of detail about times and distances; again not much was written about the footplate and its equipment. E. L. Ahrons, however, in his 'Locomotive and Train Working in the Nineteenth Century' series in *The Railway Magazine*, includes some comments on the engine cab and on the harsh working conditions of its crew.

By about 1910 more books began to appear in which readers were let into some of the hitherto secret aspects of railway engineering and operation. *All About Railways: A Book For Boys* by F. S. Hartnell (1910) went so far as to describe the interlocking of points and signals, variable cut-off, superheating and continuous automatic brakes. A random sample from the 'railway' publications on sale in 1914 discloses that in *The Railway Magazine* for July to December there are no illustrations of the interior of a locomotive cab and there are no references to enginemen and their work.

Between 1919 and 1939 there was an increase in the number of books that attempted to explain more about the workings of the railway. They had the benefit, denied those of earlier decades, of the improvements in photographic illustrations, so they were not just thousands of words interspersed by a few, often crudely retouched, photographs. Unfortunately, many of their authors were neither railwaymen nor well-informed laymen. They were often inaccurate, of which the contributors to Arthur Mee's *Children's Encyclopaedia* are good examples of providing risible captions to illustrations. During these years came the weekly partworks written by panels of authors. These usually included articles that provided the reader with an insight into the technology of the railways. However, they tended to be 'padded out' with what might be called 'tourist brochure' stories. For example, *The Wonderful Railways of Outer Ruritania* is illustrated with views of the mountain scenery but provides little information about the trains, their locomotives and the enginemen.

Second World War restrictions on the supply of paper limited the number of new railway books. Rixon Bucknall's *Our Railway History* of 1944 is an example of a condensed illustrated history that overcame the publication restrictions of wartime. It led to the later works of Hamilton Ellis, a prolific writer of railway histories. Not for him the astringent facts of C. J. Allen and O. S. Nock. He developed a unique writing style replete with flowery language. The following is a typical extract from his *The Trains We Loved* (1947):

'Here on the Midland, the syncopated double exhaust of the two Kirtley 2-4-0s settles down sweetly to the long soft roar of engines running at speed.'

Admire his style or not, at least it was different. Of course, it was doubtful at the time whether the enginemen appreciated the 'syncopated double exhaust'. They had other matters to think about: such as, 'They say it's thick fog near the Trent,' and, 'Can't think where Kentish Town got this coal.'

In his *The Beauty Of Old Trains* Hamilton Ellis, in his observations on railway aesthetics, made one of his few comments on footplate design. It is worth quoting because it provides an excellent summary of the subject:

'Of other details, cabs were a weak point of British locomotives in the mid-nineteenth-century years. Many were not cabs at all, but mere beggarly weatherboards with round spectacle glasses, supposed to save the enginemen's eyes from grit, cinders and driving hail. Sometimes the top was bent over, even far enough to form an apologetic roof. Kirtley on the Midland tried bringing this tin-tray roof right back over the footplate and securing it to a pair of uprights, without, however, any side-sheets. The best he achieved was an abominable rattle as the thing gradually worked loose. Drivers preferred to lean out at the side, braving whatever might strike their eyes. The habit, deep-seated, survives to this day [c1950], and gives to all experienced British steam locomotive drivers that shrewd, screwed-up expression which is the mark of their calling. They are forbidden to wear goggles, and doubtless would despise the idea. Your French mecanicien wears goggles, and is punished if he drives without them.'

Perhaps the general criticism that could be levelled at the majority of 'railway' writers of the 20th century, as with the 19th, was their failure adequately to describe the working conditions of footplate and shed. C. J. Allen and O. S. Nock concentrated on times, distances, cut-offs and regulator positions. Their output of words was prodigious, but both tended to push the crew into the background of their words. Nock used some of his ration of words to describe the passing countryside and the sky, but allocated few words to the heat, oil and coal dust of the footplate, and surprisingly, considering his signalling background, was sparing with descriptions of that subject.

E. H. Livesay wrote extensively in *The Engineer* of his footplate experiences and included details of the cab.

Another of the railway 'names' was W. A. Tuplin. Whether or not you agreed with all his many pronouncements on locomotive design, his writing pulled no punches. Boiler pressures much above 175psi were anathema to him. In his many drawings of 'improved' versions of famous engine types, he usually abandoned Victorian and Edwardian curves and embellishments. Overall, he was perhaps the most active iconoclast of all time when it came to writing about those who designed locomotives. In addition to his vigorous criticisms, many of his books on the engines of a specific company included a fictional account of a ride on the footplate. These descriptions provide the reader with an insight into the work and difficulties faced by engine crews, and in this respect he was one of the few who thought about the layout of the controls. If a lever of valve could not be reached without body contortions, he said so. If the driver could not see ahead or the firedoor was set too high, he said so. In a typical paragraph in his *North Western Steam* he evokes the skill of the fireman:

'I dig up a shovel full of coal, swing back, shout "Right", the yellow-hot door moves in and up, white heat hits me but, half-blind, I swing hard at it with the shovel, clanging it down on the door-ring so that the large coal shoots on but the small flies up in a burst of sparks and the door comes down and cuts off the heat. I slide the shovel under the coal-heap and then the same again.'

There has always been a need for books written with 'hands-on' experience and which describe both technology and working conditions. A later generation of authors includes R. H. N. Hardy, whose *Steam in the Blood* (1971), his 'Stratford for Ever' series in *Steam World* and in others evoke in the reader's mind a clear image of oil, grime and dust. He had the advantage, as a writer, of having worked his way up from Premium Apprentice on the LNER to top management in BR. On the way up he fired, oiled, drove and repaired locomotives

and managed running sheds. His many experiences give an authentic flavour to his words.

One author in particular devoted 14 pages of his 250 to detailed descriptions of the cab and its fittings, a proportion much higher than that allocated by some authors; this was H. J. Campbell Cornwell in his biography of William Stroudley. D. L. Smith's collection of articles combined in *Tales of the Glasgow & South Western* (1961) and his *Legends of the GSWR in LMS Days* (1980) are good examples of writing about train operations that were conducted in the face of difficult circumstances. Adrian Vaughan, in his *Signalman's Morning* (1981), *Signalman's Twilight* (1983) and *Signalman's Nightmare* (1987), provides detailed descriptions of train operating on the one-time GWR main line. Although he was signalman, he did not write in isolation of the problems faced by signalmen: he also acknowledged the difficulties imposed on drivers and signalmen by parsimonious and ill-judged changes to the signalling system. John Betjeman must also be mentioned because he, perhaps more than any other writer, described with a mixture of nostalgia and fact the part played in our lives by the steam railway of these islands. But he usually ignored the footplate.

What of the milestones in railway literature and their attention to the footplate and enginemen? George Dow's *Great Central* in three volumes and MacDermot's *History of the Great Western Railway* in two volumes are representative of a range of comprehensive histories published in the last century. However, a reader seeking information about footplates and their crews might be disappointed. The one-time doyen of steam locomotive design and technology, André Chapelon, in his monumental book *La Locomotive à Vapeur* (1952), made few references to the position of the controls relative to the driver and the fireman. In a companion book, *La Machine Locomotive*, Chapelon and Sauvage made no specific reference to the best locations for the controls. In A. M. Bell's *Locomotives* (c1938) only two pages are allocated to the subject of the cab and its controls. The comprehensive 600-page *Railway Mechanical Engineering* of 1923 virtually ignores the subject.

The presumably editorial decisions not to include the design and equipment of footplates are in contrast to the attention paid to the design of the aircraft cockpit and the role of the pilot in aviation writings. One might gain the impression that the locomotive cab was of little importance. Perhaps the majority of editors and authors relied on readers assuming that, as the footplate and its controls of Stephenson's *Locomotion* had proved perfectly satisfactory for 100 years there was, therefore, no need to discuss the subject any further.

Books about accidents usually achieved good sales figures. An important book on this subject, because it became a benchmark for others, was L. T. C. Rolt's *Red for Danger* of 1955. In 1966 came O. S. Nock's *Historic Railway Disasters*. By the very nature of the subject, the role of footplatemen and signalmen has to be given prominence. Stanley Hall's *Danger Signals*, and his other books, deal with accidents objectively and without sensation. Unfortunately, other writers, particularly for television documentaries, have allowed sensationalism to dominate factual accuracy.

Ian Allan's *ABC of Locomotives* booklets, which started to appear in the post-Second World War years, were much appreciated by that particular species of enthusiast, the number collectors. They were the railway 'philatelists'. Many of those who spent their pocket money on the ABCs were potential buyers of books from which they learned more about the technology of the footplate. By 1970, if not earlier, there was such a wealth of titles available that to acquire them all was beyond the pocket of most enthusiasts.

IMAGES

Finding illustrations, including photographs, of footplate crews at work is difficult. There are not many. Why do artists and photographers avoid what after all can be a very dramatic subject? Is it because the technology is not understood or it is not an attractive subject? Those artists who have attempted to depict a footplate crew in action have often relied on the glare from the open firedoor to accentuate their features. A good image that has rarely been used is that of the driver of an express locomotive travelling at speed. He half leans out of the window with his hand close to the brake lever. This is an image of someone at a high stage of alert with his body framed by the figure of the fireman swinging his shovel. This is an opportunity to evoke an image in paint of speed, steam, smoke, glare and power.

Michael Freeman in his *Railways and the Victorian Imagination* (Yale University Press, 1999) includes hundreds of illustrations, but only about six depict enginemen on the footplate. It is doubtful that the author deliberately included only a few. More than likely the picture editor discovered that, as others have, there were few to be had.

Few of the illustrations of the first two decades of the steam railway depict signals. For example, the beautiful engravings of J .C. Bourne convey much about the railway scene of the 1840s but there a few signals. This is not surprising because, compared with later decades, there were few. His engraving of a skewed-arch wooden bridge on the GWR near Bristol includes a very tall crossbar signal. Those artists who were unfamiliar with the technology of lineside signals were sometimes confused over which direction an arm should

A sketch to suggest the type of dramatic depiction of the footplate that is rarely attempted by professional artists. *Author*

point; this was often caused because some were positioned to the right of the track, an error of observation that continued to be made until the end of semaphore signals. An often-published illustration of an LNWR train emerging from Primrose Hill Tunnel suggests that right-hand running was used and the signals were also on the right. The question it poses is: was the artist wrong or did the LNWR , for a time, adopt right-hand running?

Hamilton Ellis was also an artist, and produced many oil paintings of locomotives and trains in suitable settings. The majority were of 'photographic' accuracy, but with some he lost control of the perspective so that buffer beams in particular gave the impression that they had been in a collision. When he depicted the enginemen on the footplate they gave the impression, from their wooden stance, that they were just passengers and had nothing to do with the engine. Other 'railway' authors have been tempted to try their hand with a paintbox and brush but, in general, few have produced other than amateurish pictures. However, putting these criticisms of artists to one side, undoubtedly few have considered the footplate a worthwhile subject.

FOOTPLATE AND SIGNALS AND FILMS

Words about the railway have often been adapted for the cinema and in turn for TV, and the footplate is often one of the most important 'locations' in a film. It provides an audience with a dramatic background of sound and movement. Sometimes it is the real thing, sometimes a mock-up. Even when a producer decides that there is enough money to hire a real locomotive and shoot scenes on its footplate, the film's editor is quite likely to spoil the effect by splicing in a number of different locomotive types for the linking shots. A famous example is in *Night Mail*, where at least three different footplates were used for when the train crosses the border, one of which was of a right-hand-drive Midland Compound, whereas the others were the cabs of left-hand-drive locomotives. But, of course, the director and the editor worked on the principle that 'the viewers will not notice' – after all, 'a cab is a cab is a cab'. In contrast, the film *Elizabethan Express* by British

Transport Films (BTF) included shots on the footplate of an 'A4' 4-6-2 as it pulled its train between London and Edinburgh. They were some of the best ever shown. However, for some the film was spoiled by the banal commentary spoken in verse. BTF made dozens of films, but few, apart from *Elizabethan Express*, included shots of the footplate of a steam locomotive.

A prime example of mixing up library shots of footplates and locomotives occurs in a Hollywood version of a Sherlock Holmes story. Holmes and Watson take a train from London Euston to the North. The studio reconstruction of LMS coaches results in nothing like the real thing. The train is about to start, so the viewer is shown the footplate of the locomotive. The driver's hand is on the regulator. But the gloved hand is that of an American engineer who somehow has got on to the footplate of a 'Royal Scot' and installed himself and his controls on the fireman's side. Thereafter, the train carries on north, and at intervals it changes locomotive type – GWR 'King' rushes into a tunnel and emerges at the other end as a Gresley 'Pacific'!

When it comes to dialogue Hollywood sometimes gets itself in a muddle. For example, real French locomotives and trains were used in the making of *The Train* (1964). In one scene the star, Burt Lancaster, says 'Take the stick.' He meant to say 'regulator' – he was not in the cockpit of an aircraft but on the footplate of a Nord 4-6-0. *La Bête Humaine* (1938) is one of the few films in which the actors do not get in the way of the locomotives and of their footplates in particular, and should have been used as an example by some British film-makers. It includes shots by a camera mounted in the coal space of the tender of a one-time Etat 'Pacific'. The driver and fireman are seen at work acknowledging clear signals and operating the water pick-up gear. The star of the film, Jean Gabin, achieved such an excellent grasp of the role of the *mecanicien* that it was acknowledged by the engine crews at Le Havre who presented him with an inscribed oilcan. Many of the British 'railway' films of the 1920s and '30s included scenes on the footplate, some the real thing, others mock-ups. However, in most the driver appears to be unconcerned about the appearance of any signals, and the signalmen to the progress of the train.

The authors of sensational fiction with a

'runaway train' plot often provided, and still do, an example of never letting the facts get in the way of a good story. Other trains and signals are unnecessary technicalities that have to be ignored, otherwise the drama on the footplate would come to a standstill. This also applies in fiction and particularly with the plot of films. Those that have had a railway setting rarely acknowledge the true facts of operating. In order to provide drama, such essential features as signals and automatic continuous brake have more often than not been ignored. As for interlocking, this safety aspect of railway operation has more often than not been put on one side by writers. The fact that a signalman could not move the points at the last minute in front of a speeding train must have spoiled many an author's attempt to provide exciting action! Such irritating items of technology have often had to be ignored in order to enhance the drama. On real railways, trains proceed in accordance with strictly enforced rules, their every move being governed by mandatory regulations, whereas in the film studio writers, producers, directors and others often assume that the trains, the signals, the track and the points can be 'played with' as if they were a toy train set.

Despite the difficulty, trains are depicted being divided while moving, yet neither part stops automatically. We often read and see in film and on TV a train being deliberately divided by the 'baddie' 'pulling the pin' on a buckeye coupling or lifting the shackle of a tight screw-link coupling. Such operations, on a moving train, are not easy. In the film *The Flying Scotsman* there were some realistic shots inside the cab of a 'Pacific' involving a fight between the driver and the fireman. Nigel Gresley was none too pleased in 1929 when he was shown the film; he objected strongly to seeing the deliberately detached part of the train continue to follow on, despite its automatic brakes. Furthermore it proceeded along the up line, whereas all the previous action had been on the down line. Your author stood alongside the Hertford Loop, beside his father who was involved with the film, as a set of coaches was propelled north along the up line, then wrong way through a trailing crossover back onto the down line. As for signals, their function was put on one side. Presumably, HM Railway Inspectorate was on holiday that day.

Another film that the author witnessed in production was *The Wrecker* of 1928. This involved the wrecking not of a model but a real train on the Basingstoke-Alton line. Again, many liberties were taken with the facts, but at least the real driver and fireman filmed on the footplate were replaced by dummies at the last moment.

Hitchcock's *The Lady Vanishes* of 1938 includes unconvincing model trains and scenery as well as mounting the smoke deflectors of the locomotive the wrong way round. So as not to let the facts get in the way of the action, two of the characters, a musician and a cricketing enthusiast, climb on to the footplate and manage immediately to understand how to drive an engine. Shots on the footplate of the supposedly continental-type locomotive reveal the regulator of a 'Schools' Class 4-4-0. In contrast, the producers of *Train of Events* (1949) took the trouble to use the footplate of a real locomotive.

Even if the cameramen have filmed the arms of semaphore signals moving, the subsequent editing process often results in a shot of a signal arm in the 'on' position followed by the train leaving, then a shot of the signal in the 'off' position. It must be frustrating for those railway people who are asked to advise on technicalities to see in the final version of a film that their advice and explanations of how things work have been either edited out or put in the wrong sequence. But, again, does it matter? Never let the facts spoil a good story!

In recent years there have been a number of television programmes about railways from which have been derived books. Just one detail from a TV series illustrates the way facts have been distorted. The viewer was shown the oil lamp in the cab of a GWR locomotive. The presenter imparted the sensational news that the lamp was there especially to illuminate the water gauge when passing through the Severn Tunnel, despite the fact that there were other tunnels on the GWR. Even if a television documentary includes shots inside the cab of a locomotive the viewer is often deprived of a sight of the controls because the film editor considers that the presenter's body and face are far more important.

Concern for the blood pressure of railway enthusiasts should prompt the following warning at the beginning of any 'railway' film: 'Viewers are warned that this film may contain scenes of appalling inaccuracies and distortions of facts.'

8
OTHER MOTIVE POWER CONTROL POSITIONS

The Victorian steam locomotive and its successors had a control position in the rear of the bulk of the machine when related to the usual direction of running. By contrast, the non-steam types of power unit, after some undecided steps during the early years of electric traction, settled for a control position close to one end of the unit, sometimes duplicated at the other end. The driver no longer had to contest his view ahead with the body of the machine, and wide arcs of view were usually available. At the same time the driver was no longer able to shelter behind the bulk of the machine in the event of trouble. Irrespective of the type of power, electric or diesel, the term 'footplate' no longer became applicable.

The early electric trains and locomotives perpetuated the standing position for the driver, following the example set by the tramways. As with the steam locomotive footplate, controls and instruments were not always positioned with the needs of the driver in mind.

SHAPE AND LOCATION

In general, the shape and the location of the driver's position for non-steam units could be classified as follows:

1 Flat-fronted, with good forward horizontal and vertical arcs of view, as in the majority of British electric train units. This type of front is usually dictated by the need to be able to couple with other units.

2 Stepped or 'automobile' front, in which the

driver's eye-point is about 2 metres from the front of the train, as in some British diesel-electrics.

3 'Aerodynamically' shaped nose, examples being the French TGV, 'Eurostar', the British HST and Virgin 'Pendolino' 'Voyager'.

The first diesel-electric 'streamlined' trains in the USA positioned the engineer (driver) close to the nose. The diesel-electric locomotives that followed had an 'automobile'-shaped profile with the engineer's position set back from the nose. This configuration allowed the industrial designer great scope for developing an attractive shape and use of colour. However, the infrastructure and the operating environment of the railroads in North America did not keep up with this technology. The majority of the intersections of the railroad and the highway were without any form of safety equipment other than warning signs advising car drivers that a train was approaching. An 800-ton passenger train moving at 60mph needed at least half a mile in which to pull up after an emergency application of the brakes. If an engineer spotted a car stuck across the track, or a reckless car driver about to contest the right of way, all he could do was duck and hope that the car did not derail the train. The heavy diesel locomotives usually won the contest with a car, but sometimes not with a truck.

By the 1950s consideration started to be given to protecting the locomotive crew during a collision, particularly as road vehicles were larger and heavier than those when the diesel locomotive first entered the scene. The solution adopted was to strengthen the structure at the front sufficiently to protect the crew. Aesthetics had to give way to the real world. The elegantly shaped fronts of the 1940s generation of locomotives gave way to a strictly utilitarian arrangement of the steps, platforms and other appendages, such as brake pipes and multiple-unit connections.

Another factor that had to be considered in North American railroad operation, and one that directly affected the person in control, was the deliberate stoning of and sometimes shooting at the engineer's cab. When passing through some areas he or she had the task of watching not just for signals and the condition of the track ahead but scanning the line on each side in order to anticipate an attack. With most electric or diesel multiple unit trains the driver is right at the front. This is a very vulnerable position when someone hurls a rock or drops a slab of concrete from an overbridge. In these circumstances such ergonomic requirements as good arcs of forward view have to be set aside in favour of the smallest practicable armoured and grilled window. An example is with the high-speed trains operating between Washington and New York. In some parts of the USA industrial safety goggles have to

be worn by train crews to protect them from missiles launched by disaffected or bored youths.

The principal control in the cab of an electric or diesel train is usually a lever moving in the horizontal plane. The earliest electric train control positions were similar to those of the contemporary tramcars. The control characteristics of the series direct-current motor required the step-by-step withdrawal or insertion of resistances and the means for operating in series or in parallel in order to accelerate or slow down. Therefore, a common item of equipment was a vertical control pedestal with a lever or wheel mounted on the top. The Swiss preferred a wheel-type control on their AC locomotives and trains. At one time those few people, including journalists, who argued that trains were steered quoted Swiss films that showed a driver frequently turning the wheel. However, they had not observed that sometimes he turned the wheel in the opposite direction from a bend in the track!

The foregoing stereotype control is now being superseded by more sophisticated systems, as for example a lever in the vertical plane alongside the driver. When pushed forward it commands the train to accelerate. Similarly the brake lever moves in the vertical plane. On the London Underground some trains have only one principal

The driver's control position at the front of a Virgin 'Pendolino' electric multiple unit on the West Coast Main Line. The 'Pendolino' is able to lean into curves and travel at speeds undreamed of in the 1840s.
Milepost 92½

control lever, which combines both acceleration and retardation in one lever in order to start, increase speed or slow down and stop. It simultaneously proportions power and braking.

MONITORING THE DRIVER'S ATTENTION

With very fast trains (200kmph-plus) the driver's attention to the signals is continuously monitored. If the driver fails to respond to lineside or in-cab signals or makes no changes to any of the controls after a certain time, a monitoring system reduces power and applies the brakes.

MONITORING AND CONTROLLING POWER

Many of today's electric locomotives and multiple-unit power cars can exert 1,000hp per axle. Power has therefore to be carefully applied in order to achieve the maximum acceleration and avoid wheel-slip. From a start or after a speed restriction, an on-board computer can take control of the application of power. Gone are the days when a driver's skill could be measured by his ability to accelerate his train without letting the locomotive's wheels slip.

'PILOTING' A HIGH-SPEED TRAIN

The driver of a high-speed train – one capable of around 200kmph – is in an operating environment analogous to that of a jet aircraft pilot. Both are isolated to some degree from the real world and therefore verbal and visual information is needed to keep them either directly in the control loop or to enable them to monitor progress. The driver of the Victorian steam locomotive was in a man-machine interface in which there were very direct inputs to the senses in the form of sounds and vibrations. These, together with the need to keep a constant lookout ahead for signals and landmarks from which to check progress, kept the driver fully aware of what was going on. In aviation this is termed 'situation awareness'. In April 2007 an SNCF TGV attained a speed of 357mph, or 500ft/sec, which meant that a sudden obstruction a mile ahead would have been collided with within 10 seconds, unless the train could be brought to a standstill by decelerating at a phenomenal rate. 'Fasten your seat belts please'!

Foretelling the future of the control positions of trains requires the author's neck to be stuck out to a dangerous degree. Indications are, when considering present technologies, that at some time in the future there will be no one sitting at the front of the train monitoring speed and distance information. Many passengers have come to accept that their train is 'driverless' – in London are the examples of the Victoria Line and the Docklands Light Railway. On many industrial bulk carrier lines trains have no human crew and are operated fully automatically from a central control; most of these are, of course, isolated systems. Lineside signals will eventually become redundant and the Global Positioning System, which can already pinpoint accurately the position of a train, could become the primary system for separating trains one from each other.

Far removed from the world of the steam locomotive footplate is use of a radio link and a handheld portable control unit used by an 'operator' to control remotely a diesel-electric shunting engine. It can be used when standing on the locomotive's front steps or when standing to one side of the track in the best position to monitor its movements. Alternatively the operator could be many miles away and monitoring his decisions on a television screen.

Over 160 years we have moved from the open footplate and harsh operating conditions of the first steam locomotives to no footplates and with the 'crew' sitting in comfort before a video display and a few buttons on a control panel far from the trains.

SELECTED BIBLIOGRAPHY

Ahrons, E. L. *Locomotive and Train Working in the Nineteenth Century* (Heffer, 1953)

Allen, C. J. *The Great Eastern Railway* (Ian Allan, 1968)

Brown, F. A. S. *Nigel Gresley, Locomotive Engineer* (Ian Allan, 1962)

Byles, C. B. *The First Principles of Railway Signalling* (Railway Gazette, 1918)

Campbell Cornwell, H. J. *William Stroudley, Craftsman of Steam* (David & Charles, 1968)

Chapelon, A. *La Locomotive à Vapeur* (Bailliere, Paris, 1952; English translation by G. W. Carpenter, Camden Miniatures, 2000)

Coombs, L. F. E. *Steam Locomotive Ergonomics* ('Applied Ergonomics', 1973 4.1, IPC)
The Harrow Railway Disaster 1952 (David & Charles, 1977)

Cox, E. S. *World Steam In The 20th Century* (Ian Allan, 1969)

Earnshaw, Prof A., article in *Steam World*, December 1995

Freeman, M. *Railways and the Victorian Imagination* (Yale, 1999)

Hall, S. *Danger Signals* (Ian Allan, 1987)

Hamilton, J. A. B. *British Railway Accidents of the Twentieth Century* (Allen & Unwin, 1967)

Hardy, R. H. N. *Steam In The Blood* (Ian Allan, 1975)
'Stratford For Ever' series in *Steam World*

Highet, C. *Scottish Locomotive History 1831-1923* (Allen & Unwin, 1970)

Holcroft, H. *Locomotive Adventure* Vols I and II (Ian Allan, 1965)
An Outline Of Great Western Locomotive Practice 1837-1947 (Ian Allan, 1971)

Hoole, K. *The North Eastern Atlantics* (Roundhouse Books, 1965)

Jackman, M. *Bricklayers Arms: Southern Steam From The Footplate* (David & Charles, 1976)

Kichenside, G. M. and Williams, Alan *British Railway Signalling* (Ian Allan, 1968)

Meacher, C. *LNER Footplate Memories* (Bradford Barton)

Morgan, B. *Railways: Civil Engineering* (Arrow, 1973)

Nock, O. S. *British Locomotives At Work* (Lake, 1947)
British Locomotives Of The 20th Century (3 Vols) (Patrick Stephens Ltd, 1983-5)
Historic Railway Disasters (Ian Allan, 1966)
Fifty Years of Railway Signalling (Institution of Railway Signalling Engineers, 1962)
Locomotives of the North Eastern (Ian Allan, 1954)

Powell, A. J. *Living With London Midland Steam* (Ian Allan, 1977)
Royal Scots of the LMS (Ian Allan, 1970)

Rayner Wilson, H. *The Safety of British Railways* (King & Son, 1909)

Reynolds, M. *Locomotive Engine Driving* (Lockwood, 1877)
Engine-Driving Life (Lockwood, 1881)

Rich, F. *Some Details of Footplate Design Affecting the Footplate Man* (Institution of Locomotive Engineers, 1958)

Rolt, L. T. C. *Red For Danger* (Bodley Head, 1955)

Rutherford, M. 'Provocations' series in *Backtrack*

Smith, D. L. *Tales of the Glasgow and South Western Railway* (Ian Allan, 1970)
Legends Of The Glasgow and South Western

Railway in LMS Days (David & Charles, 1980)

Snell, J. B. *Mechanical Engineering Railways* (Longman, 1971)

Summers, L. A. Written communication and various articles in *Backtrack*, eg November 2008, pp646-653

Townend, P. N. *East Coast Pacifics At Work* (Ian Allan, 1982)

Top Shed (Ian Allan, 1977)

Tuplin, W. A. *Great Northern Steam* (Ian Allan, 1971)

Great Western Steam (Allen & Unwin, 1958)

Midland Steam (David & Charles, 1973)

North Western Steam (Allen & Unwin, 1963)

Vanns, M. A. *An Illustrated History of Signalling* (Ian Allan, 1998)

Vaughan, A. *Signalman's Morning* (John Murray, 1981)

Signalman's Twilight (John Murray, 1983)

Signalman's Nightmare (John Murray, 1987)

Warren, J. G. H. *A Century of Locomotive Building* (Reid, 1923)

INDEX

Accidents, 36, 43, 49, 50, 105; Abbots Ripton (1876) 41; Bourne End (1945) 107; Grantham (1906) 105; Harrow (1952) 90-92, 106, 113; Lewisham (1957) 105; Ludlow (1957) 111; Norton Fitzwarren (1890) 35; Milton (1955) 110, 111; Norton Fitzwarren (1940) 106-107; Salisbury (1906) 105

Artists, treatment of loco cabs by 19, 20, 120-121

Ashpans, poor design of 67-68

Beattie, Joseph 61

Beyer-Garratt locomotives 82

Blenkinsop, John 15, 19

Boiler explosions 17

Brakes, development of 21-22, 24, 43, 67; air 64, 77; Brakes Act, 1878 52;continuous 51-52; in emergencies 36, 43; quick-acting 77; self-acting 50; risk of snatching couplings 50; standardisation of 77; vacuum 22, 51, 52, 64, 73, 77; Webb chain brake 51 see also Westinghouse

British Railways Standard locomotives 93-97; 'Britannias' 93-96; No 71000 96

Bulleid, O. V. S. 68, 84, 86-89; 'Leader' Class 65, 87, 89

Bury, Edward 17-18, 45; *Liverpool* 17

Cab signalling systems 44-46, 108-109, 112-113; Automatic Train Control (ATC) (GWR) 45, 70, 108, 111, 112; BR (AWS) 113; Hudd Automatic/Advanced Warning System 102, 108, 113

Cabs, development of 52-53, 89; first 18; of tank engines 54

Caledonian Railway 22, 31, 64, 77

Channel Tunnel railway (1920) 108-109

Clay Cross Tunnel 33

Clayton Tunnel 34

Coal, ease of shovelling from tender 99-100; ready supply of 65; replaces coke 48

Coligny-Welch illuminated Distant signal 39, 101

Communication cord 43

Compound locomotives 75-76, 100

Crampton locomotives 62, 64

Cut-off/reverser 11, 48, 63, 69, 70, 93, 96 see also Reversing lever

Detonators 36-37

Dickens, Charles 45, 114-115

Diesel locomotives 123-125; Virgin 'Pendolino' 123, 124

Drivers, distraction of 36, 105, 106; drifting smoke affecting visibility 109-110; driving techniques of 11, 92-93; 'expectation', dangers of 36, 105-106; knowledge of road and signalling 25, 31, 43-44, 101, 102; on earliest locomotives 15-16; on diesels and electrics 123-125; 'view ahead' 23; remedies for faults 93; response to signals 29, 41; seats for 75

Drummond, Dugald 67, 70, 112

Electric locomotives 123-125

Electricity on steam locomotives 98-99

Ellis, C. Hamilton 118

Ergonomics, development of concept 16, 84, 87, 92

Fallplates 96-97

Firemen 78, 99-100, 111; space on footplate for 47, 64, 84; responsibility for applying brakes 52

Fletcher, Edward 56-58

Footplate crew, clothing of 49; evolved from stationary engine operators 14-15, 16, 17; injuries to 65; promotion opportunities 66; social standing of 10, 22, 65

Footplates, earliest 15; consideration given to design and layout 9, 16, 17-18, 47, 66-67, 80-82; dangers and inconveniences of 48-49, 65, 66, 68, 93; electricity on 98; in art 120-121; in films 121-122; in literature 114-120; position of crew on 31, 64, 65, 92-93; railings added 47; 'view ahead' 23, 30, 34, 58

Fowler, Henry 72

France 48, 63-64, 66, 70, 75, 97-98, 123; signalling in 11, 27, 31, 37-38, 41, 46, 105

Franco-Crosti boiler 110

Furness Railway 39, 51

Germany, railways in 31, 48

Glasgow & South Western Railway 22, 31, 33, 37, 53, 54, 67

Grates, rocking 82
Great Central Railway 38, 39, 53, 67, 80, 81, 112; loco cabs 73-75
Great Eastern Railway 52, 53, 62, 77, 99, 112
Great North of Scotland Railway 22, 31, 77
Great Northern Railway 32, 38, 39, 41, 53, 63, 77, 93
Great Western Railway 27,29, 30, 35, 38, 39, 43, 54, 63, 68, 71, 72, 77, 93, 106, 110; loco cabs 54-55, 68-70
Gresley, Nigel 75, 81, 95, 109, 110; cabs of 77-80

Hackworth, Timothy 17, 47; *Royal George* 17
Headlamp codes 35
Hedley, William 15
Highland Railway 109
Holmes, M. 61

Industrial Health Research Board 92
Injectors 48, 100

Kemble, Frances 19

Lancashire & Yorkshire Railway 31, 35, 39, 43-44, 53, 62, 75, 103
Lickey Incline 42
Liverpool & Manchester Railway 17, 19, 27, 33
London & Birmingham Railway 44
London & North Eastern Railway 75, 79, 81, 106, 109, 113
London & North Western Railway 31, 34, 39, 51, 52, 63, 67, 70, 77, 109; loco cabs 58-59
London & South Western Railway 28, 44, 61, 67, 70, 77, 112
London, Brighton & South Coast Railway 31, 34, 38, 40, 43, 44, 45, 46, 77; loco cabs 59-60
London, Chatham & Dover Railway 46, 51, 73, 77
London, Midland & Scottish Railway 70-71, 79, 80, 82-85, 101-102, 107, 110, 113; Derby drawing office 71, 72
London, Tilbury & Southend Railway 77

McDonnell, Alexander 57, 72
Manchester Sheffield & Lincolnshire Railway 22, 35, 38
Mechanical stokers 89
Metropolitan/Metropolitan District Railways 39, 41, 44, 51, 101, 112

Midland Railway 22, 29, 71, 72, 77, 80, 101; loco cabs 60-61
Mines, tramways in 13, 14
Mutual improvement classes 65-66

Newark Brake Trials 22, 52, 59
Newcastle & Carlisle Railway 31
North British Railway 22, 74, 77; loco cabs 61
North Eastern Railway 29, 41, 44, 45-46, 53, 75, 77, 104, 112; loco cabs 55-58, 72-73
North Staffordshire Railway 67

Plateways 13
Points, interlocking of 26

Railway companies, resistance to change 50, 66, 80
Railway Inspectorate 49
'Railway Time' 25
Rainhill Trials 17
Ramsbottom, John 58
Raven, Vincent 46, 73, 112
Regulation of Railways Act, 1889 43
Regulator 11, 47-48, 75, 81, 82, 96
Reversing lever 48
Reynolds, Michael 11, 115-116
Robinson, J. G. 73-75

Safety valves 17, 20
Sand boxes 68
Sheffield, Ashton-under-Lyne & Manchester Railway, signals 28, 49
Sherlock Holmes 117
Signalling systems, development of 10, 26; 'Block system' 34-35, 36; early 'policemen' 25, 28, 30, 33; development of interlocking 29-30; 'Lock and block' 42; 'Lock, block and brake' 49-50; speed signalling 107-108; standardisation of 105; 'time interval' 33, 34
Signals, audible (gongs, etc) 105; choice of red and green aspects 27; choice of yellow for caution 101; colour light 107-108; 'disc and crossbar' 27, 28; Distant ('auxiliary') signals 28-30, 38-39, 40, 101; distinguishing different types 41-42, 101, 105; flashing-light 101-102, 108; 'geographical' positioning of at junctions 44, 103; lineside, introduction of 25, 29; lower-quadrant 38, 39; naval signalling, influence of 26-27; night-time aspects 29, 39; position and sighting of 10, 29, 30-32, 39, 106; rotating boards 26, 28; shapes

of 26-27, 33; smoke affecting visibility 41, 58, 109-110; 'somersault' 39; subsidiary 102, 103; three-position 34-35, 38, 102
Single-track lines, regulation of 21, 105-106
Smoke deflectors 109-110
Somerset & Dorset Joint Railway 72, 81
South Eastern & Chatham Railway 51, 77
South Eastern Railway 45, 101
Southern Railway 68, 81, 86-89, 104
SPADS (Signals Passed at Danger) 98
'Specific end deterioration' 106
Speed of trains 25, 34, 36, 60, 125; temporary speed restrictions 107-108
Stanier, William 82
Steam engines, stationary 14-15
Steam locomotives, brakes on 21, 50-51; controls of 16, 78, 94, 95; early simplicity of 20; increasing standardisation of 62-63, 64; lack of advances in safety 66-67
Stephenson, George 16, 50; *Locomotion* and 'Killingworth' locos 16, 17, 19, 21, 31; 'Rocket' locos 19, 21
Stephenson, Robert 18, 19-20, 48, 55; *Patentee* 21; 'Planet' locos 18, 20, 21, 47
Stockton & Darlington Railway 17, 47, 56
Stroudley, William 59-60

Telegraph, electric 33-34, 42
Trevithick, Richard 12, 15

United States, railways in 18-19, 31, 36, 52, 123, 124; signalling 11

Valve gear, development of 20-21; Caprotti 96

Wartime, effect on locomotive crews 89-90
Water scoop 100
Webb, Francis 51, 70
Westinghouse brake 22, 52, 59-60, 73
Whistle, locomotive, use of 42, 105
Woodhead Tunnel 33
Worsdell, T. W. and Wilson 57-58, 73